TECHNIQUES AND APPLICATIONS OF EXPERT SYSTEMS IN THE CONSTRUCTION INDUSTRY

ELLIS HORWOOD SERIES IN CIVIL ENGINEERING

Series Editors
Structures: Professor R. EVANS, Department of Civil Engineering, University College, Cardiff
Hydraulic Engineering and Hydrology: Dr R. SELLIN, Department of Civil Engineering, University of Bristol
Geotechnics: Professor D. WOOD, Department of Civil Engineering, University of Glasgow
North American Editor: Professor N. G. SHRIVE, Department of Civil Engineering, University of Calgary, Canada

ML

TECHNIQUES AND APPLICATIONS OF EXPERT SYSTEMS IN THE CONSTRUCTION INDUSTRY

R. J. ALLWOOD, B.Sc., Ph.D., MICE, C.Eng.
Reader, Department of Civil Engineering
University of Technology, Loughborough

ELLIS HORWOOD LIMITED
Publishers · Chichester

Halsted Press: a division of
JOHN WILEY & SONS
New York · Chichester · Brisbane · Toronto

First published in 1989 by
ELLIS HORWOOD LIMITED
Market Cross House, Cooper Street,
Chichester, West Sussex, PO19 1EB, England
The publisher's colophon is reproduced from James Gillison's drawing of the ancient Market Cross, Chichester.

Distributors:

Australia and New Zealand:
JACARANDA WILEY LIMITED
GPO Box 859, Brisbane, Queensland 4001, Australia

Canada:
JOHN WILEY & SONS CANADA LIMITED
22 Worcester Road, Rexdale, Ontario, Canada

Europe and Africa:
JOHN WILEY & SONS LIMITED
Baffins Lane, Chichester, West Sussex, England

North and South America and the rest of the world:
Halsted Press: a division of
JOHN WILEY & SONS
605 Third Avenue, New York, NY 10158, USA

South-East Asia
JOHN WILEY & SONS (SEA) PTE LIMITED
37 Jalan Pemimpin # 05–04
Block B, Union Industrial Building, Singapore 2057

Indian Subcontinent
WILEY EASTERN LIMITED
4835/24 Ansari Road
Daryaganj, New Delhi 110002, India

© **1989 R.J. Allwood/Ellis Horwood Limited**

British Library Cataloguing in Publication Data
Allwood, R.J.
Techniques and applications of expert systems in the construction industry. —
(Ellis Horwood series in civil engineering).
1. Construction industries. Applications of expert systems
I. Title
624'.028'563

Library of Congress CIP data available

ISBN 0–7458–0538–8 (Ellis Horwood Limited)
ISBN 0–470–21389–2 (Halsted Press)

Printed in Great Britain by Hartnolls, Bodmin

Contents

To my wife and family

Preface and acknowledgements

The objective of this book is to draw to the attention of students and professionals working in the construction industry the opportunities likely to come from the new computing technology of expert systems. It is a new technology, quite different from conventional programming; a technology that provides new ways of storing and accessing knowledge, particularly knowledge obtained from experience. It is this central feature that makes expert systems so relevant to the work of architects, quantity surveyors, consulting and contracting engineers. What other industry is so dependent on knowledge in the heads of 'greybeards'? Yet how difficult it is to represent that knowledge on paper in reports or books so that other, younger heads can use it.

This book aims at explaining how expert systems offer a new solution to that problem. It is a tutorial book based on the author's experience of creating eight expert systems for industry, some of which are used as examples. To simplify the presentation, the book is divided into two parts. Part I is a simple, but not trivial, straight-through introduction to the topic avoiding side-tracking discussions of details. These are 'sign posted' to Part II where the whole topic is considered again with detail to satisfy potential users and programmers. An important theme to the book is that of storing knowledge in expert systems in a way that is comprehensible to a real expert. We have clearly failed over the past 25 years to bridge the communications gap between programmers and 'the rest'. Conventional programming languages are so concerned with the details of data processing that what knowledge is present in a program gets lost and cannot generally be understood by an outsider. Expert systems offer us a new chance to ensure that both experts and users look at the stored knowledge, understand what they see there, perhaps disagree with it, but at least identify with it and so break open the 'black boxes' we have lived with for too long. But this comprehensibility is a tender flower. It needs deliberate effort by those who write the special software of expert systems to make it possible; it needs considerable care by those who use the software to ensure that comprehensibility follows. Just what is 'comprehensibility' is a subjective matter, of course, but through this theme the author pleads for effort, erring on the excessive, to ensure that the human expert can feel comfortable about the way his knowledge is stored and used. Only then can we be confident that the potential of expert systems can be released.

Expert systems probably represent the 'blunt end' of artificial intelligence research — the sharp end is concerned with modelling common sense and fundamental knowledge, enabling automatic learning, and many other topics. It is unusual in the short history of computing that the earliest products of a new development prove so useful. The book ends with some modest speculation on what might fall out from current AI research which we in the construction industry could both understand and use.

Three items before we start: firstly, this is not an artificial intelligence text book but it is hoped that researchers and software developers will find something of interest — perhaps in the theme of comprehensibility, perhaps in the analysis of the three phases of a typical expert system, perhaps in the discussion of control and the emphasis on an object oriented approach even for the simplest knowledge base. Secondly, the author asks that expert systems are kept in perspective. Their title is unfortunate; they are only computer programs and would be better but less glamorously called 'advisers'. They are certainly not yet true experts capable of a leap in the dark. Finally, the author asks lady readers to accept that the words 'he', 'his' and 'him' are a reference to either gender.

The author would like to acknowledge the contributions made by his colleagues to the work that has led to this book, particularly those of Geoffrey Trimble, Duncan Stewart and Chris Cooper.

The extract from BS 5930: 1981 is repoduced by permission of the British Standards Institution; Fig. 3.4 is reproduced by permission of CSIRO, Melbourne; the references to the paint selection system are by permission of the Ove Arup Partnership; and the references to BREDAMP are by permission of the Director, Building Research Establishment, Department of the Environment.

Part I

1

What is an expert system? — How does it work?

1.1 THREE KEY FEATURES

An expert system is a computer program which will provide advice in a selected specialist field. The user will answer questions and will be led towards one or more recommendations. The questions are likely to be phrased in the jargon of the specialist field and the user will have the opportunity of asking the program how it arrived at its conclusion.

Three key features of expert systems distinguish them from conventional computer programs which could, in a limited sense, behave in the manner described above.

(1) The central element of an expert system is a representation of an expert's knowledge about the specialism in a form comprehensible to man and computer.
(2) That knowledge is continuously searched by sophisticated methods when the system is striving to 'solve' a user's problem.
(3) The user can be given an explanation of 'how' an answer was arrived at from the very same knowledge statements used to obtain the answer.

How knowledge can be represented in a suitable form is still a matter for research *... The most* but we shall see one popular method in the next section. Whatever form is adopted, *common* → the outcome is that an expert's knowledge can be stored in a computer file on a hard or floppy disc. Such files are often called 'knowledge bases' and the limited field of specialism is sometimes called the 'domain'. The searching of a knowledge base, the feature that so separates expert systems from conventional computer programs, is done by a special piece of software called an 'expert system shell program'. The name is quite suitable, since a shell program is nothing without a knowledge base kernel. Fig. 1.1 shows the combination of shell and knowledge base. There are already many shell programs available commercially, not unfortunately using a commonly agreed

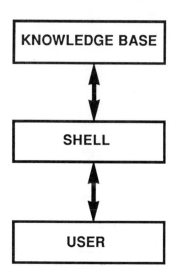

Fig. 1.1 — A shell program and a knowledge base.

form of knowledge representation. As Fig. 1.1 shows, the shell interacts with the user as well as searching the knowledge base. All questions and answers and displays are handled by the shell program, thus providing a robust and professional appearance to the expert system. One obvious advantage of the combination shown in Fig. 1.1 is that users may have access to several different knowledge bases about various specialisms but will use them through the same shell. This gives the users a consistent presentation of all questions and displays and saves them from having to learn how to run many different programs.

In this book, we shall be principally concerned with expert systems for the diagnosis of faults, the selection of materials and the offering of advice. The three features set out above will now be discussed in terms of a diagnosis system.

1.2   REPRESENTING KNOWLEDGE — BY 'RULES'

The most common form of statement to represent knowledge in an expert system is the rule. There are other forms, but every expert system shell allows rules and it is obvious that their popularity lies in their immediate comprehensibility if well phrased. We are used to rules — particularly negative rules such as 'Don't walk on the grass': although such an incomplete rule with no clear consequence would have no place in an expert system. We can define a rule for an expert system as follows:

IF a set of propositions is true
THEN some consequences follow.

Such rules are sometimes called 'production' rules since they produce a result. To turn this abstract definition into practical terms, we shall use some rules which express part of the knowledge about cracks in masonry walls to be found in

Eldridge (1976). Thus, considering the evidence of cracks in the walls of a brick-built house one could have a rule such as:

> IF the direction of the cracks is diagonal
> AND the cracks are from the damp-proof course to a window or other opening
> AND all the cracks are in one direction
> THEN the likely cause is expansion of the bricks.

This rule has three propositions, often called antecedents, joined by the word AND and so all three propositions must be true for the consequent to be true. We shall see other rules with propositions joined by OR as well. The consequent shown is, of course, one possible fault and so we have started to build a diagnostic system capable of finding the most likely fault to have caused cracks in a wall.

To a programmer this rule looks little different from an IF statement in a conventional programming language. However, there is a very big difference. The rule only applies if all the propositions are true. If one is not true, the *rule is simply cancelled and ignored*. The rule has nothing to say about the negative version of the propositions. Putting that in terms of conventional programming languages such as BASIC, FORTRAN or PASCAL, there is no ELSE clause. If a conclusion can be drawn from the negative of some or all of the propositions, that must be expressed in separate rules. (Some shells allow ELSE, a hangover from the past although it does provide an awkward means of specifying a default value — see Chapter 7.) It is important to view the rule as a single, unambiguous, watertight statement of knowledge restricted entirely to proving the truth or otherwise of the cracks being due to the expansion of the bricks. (For those interested, 'clay bricks are liable to undergo an irreversible expansion starting from the time that they leave the kiln and continuing for a period of several years . . .', Eldridge (1976).)

Here is another rule.

> IF the direction of the cracks is diagonal
> AND (cracks are tooth-shaped in a corner OR
> there are many cracks at the foundation)
> THEN the likely cause is expansion of the bricks.

These propositions are linked by OR as well as AND and brackets are used also. Some shells do not allow OR which can be overcome somewhat tediously by writing two rules for the same consequent instead of one. Brackets are essential to clarify the sequence of evaluation.

It may surprise some readers to see two rules leading to the same consequent. It is common and, of course, simply reflects the expert's view that one cause may have several effects due to the presence of other factors. Just to balance the situation, here is a last rule for a different cause of cracking.

> IF the direction of the cracks is vertical
> AND the cracks are widest at the top
> AND there is a single crack on opposite sides of the building
> THEN the likely cause is movement of the ground.

If the consequent of a rule is one of the final answers to be recommended to the user, it is called a 'goal'. Each of the three simple rules illustrated above therefore ends with a goal. That is not necessarily the case. Rules may end with consequents which are only intermediate conclusions called 'sub-goals'. Such sub-goals will appear in antecedents of other rules creating tiers of rules upon rules, linked together by their common use of the sub-goals. The jargon for this is a 'hierarchical structure'. As a simple illustration, we might relegate 'movement of the ground' in the last rule to the status of a sub-goal and include further rules using it to identify the real cause of the ground movement. One of those rules could be:

> IF the likely cause is movement of the ground
> AND the soil is a shrinkable clay
> AND the building is new
> AND the site was recently cleared of large trees
> THEN the likely cause is swelling of the clay sub-soil.

These illustrative rules adopt a rather conversational English language form and achieve a level of comprehensibility that satisfies the author. The reader should be warned that not all shell programs adopt this or a similar style. Some knowledge representations plunge to near gibberish, weakly excused by the provision of powerful facilities — particularly for using one rule many times. It is admitted that there are conflicting requirements upon the designers of shells but the author asks here and later for comprehensibility of knowledge bases to be the overriding objective of any shell developer. Users should demand it.

The illustrated rules only use the verb 'is' with the meaning of 'equals'. (It is common for shells to allow useful synonyms such as 'are'.) More general forms of rules allow new verbs to be introduced provided their meaning is defined by rules. Such knowledge representations are called predicate logic rather than the simpler propositional logic which has been shown.

Rules are widely used for expressing knowledge which can be said to be deterministic. That is knowledge which is quite unambiguous and in a black-and-white form. There are other forms of knowledge, particularly when there is a measure of uncertainty and these will be discussed in Part II.

1.3   SEARCHING A KNOWLEDGE BASE FOR 'GOALS'

The second feature of an expert system given in section 1.1, i.e. that of 'searching', is perhaps the one that most clearly distinguishes it from a conventional program. We have lived for 30 years learning that a computer obeys the statements of a program in sequence; that the order of the program statements matters; and that we must draw flow charts or other charts to ensure that we get our statements coded in the correct sequence. Of course, decision statements such as IF or jump statements such as GO TO interrupt the sequence – but only momentarily.

The rules, or other forms of knowledge statement, in a knowledge base are not processed in order. They are searched (by one of a variety of methods) to find the next best statement to process in order to most quickly arrive at an answer to a problem. Fig. 1.2 illustrates this difference graphically and the reader might equate

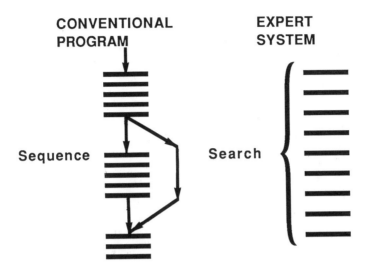

Fig. 1.2 — Sequencing and searching.

this search process with the 'reasoning' processes we humans undertake when being intelligent. We shall look immediately at one of the most popular and effective searching methods and the topic will reappear in Part II. But, before that, the reader will want answers to questions such as:

What is it searching for?
How does it start?

In the diagnostic or advice systems we are considering in this book, the search process is looking for the most likely fault causing a particular problem or the best advice to offer in a particular situation. These are the goals of the expert system and will appear as consequents of one or more rules in the knowledge base. (Not all consequents will be goals — some will be merely sub-goals which will appear as antecedents in other rules as we have just seen.) Starting the search process off is done simply by nominating to the shell program a list of goals to be evaluated in order; e.g. in our masonry cracks example, the first goal to be searched for could be 'the likely cause is ground movement' followed by 'the likely cause is expansion of the bricks'. There is a certain control available over the searching process by nominating the goals in some order, often that of the likelihood of being the right answer.

We shall look now at how one searching method works with a simple knowledge base of four rules about the cracking of masonry. Fig. 1.3 shows these rules in a

1   IF cracks are diagonal AND from dpc to opening

         AND in one direction THEN cause is expansion

2   IF cracks are vertical AND widest at top

         AND on opposite sides THEN cause is movement

3   IF cracks are vertical AND in centre of panel

         AND widest at bottom THEN cause is expansion

4   IF cracks are vertical AND near a corner

         AND it is a new building THEN cause is expansion

Fig. 1.3 — Condensed rules about cracks in masonry walls.

condensed form which frankly does not match the requirements of shells but has been adopted here to keep Figs. 1.3 to 1.6 compact. The first two are those given above in section 1.2 (not including the rule with ORs); the last two are further examples from the same source.

We start the search process off by asking the system to look for the goals 'cause is movement' and 'cause is expansion' in that order simply because ground movement is more common than brick expansion. The system looks through all the rules until it finds the first rule that refers to the first goal, i.e. rule number 2 in the figure. (Note that the ordering of rules that have the same consequent does affect the searching process by determining which rule out of the set is processed first.) The system then sets about determining whether the first proposition of this rule has been evaluated and, if not, finds if it is true or not. To do that it must ask the user a question. The simplest approach is to put the whole proposition to the user and ask if it is true or not, e.g.

'Is it true that the
cracks are vertical? — yes or no'.

The disadvantage of this is that the system will eventually have to ask

'Is it true that the
cracks are diagonal? — yes or no'.

Treating the proposition as a whole prevents the system deducing the answer to the second question from the answer to the first. A common and more efficient method is to ask the question

'What is the direction of the cracks? — vertical or diagonal'

and use the answer to evaluate the truth or not of both propositions. In doing this, we are introducing the notion of 'objects' which correspond closely to variables in programming languages. In this example the object is 'direction of the cracks'. The use of objects, the choice of their names and the possible answers to their associated questions is a major part of the task of analysing knowledge and coding an expert system.

In Fig. 1.4 we see the question, the answer and the actions taken by the search

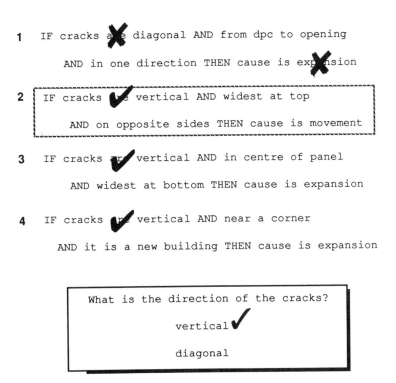

```
1    IF cracks are diagonal AND from dpc to opening

        AND in one direction THEN cause is expansion

2    IF cracks are vertical AND widest at top

        AND on opposite sides THEN cause is movement

3    IF cracks are vertical AND in centre of panel

        AND widest at bottom THEN cause is expansion

4    IF cracks are vertical AND near a corner

        AND it is a new building THEN cause is expansion


        What is the direction of the cracks?

                    vertical ✔

                    diagonal
```

Fig. 1.4 — First question, answer and consequences.

process. It will be seen that the system has taken the opportunity to spread the result of the answer — 'that the cracks are vertical' — right through the knowledge base in a chain reaction. Not only have all propositions that refer to crack direction been evaluated, but in Rule 1, because the first proposition has been proved false and because the rule only uses ANDs, the whole rule has been cancelled. This does not mean that brick expansion has been ruled out as the solution to the problem; there are still some rules about expansion which have not been cancelled. This searching process is often called 'backward chaining with opportunistic forward chaining' — backward chaining because it searches for a consequent and then evaluates the related antecedents; opportunistic forward chaining because it takes every opportunity to use the answers supplied by working forwards from each relevant proposition to evaluate all possible consequents.

In Fig. 1.5 we show the next question, answer and action. This question has been

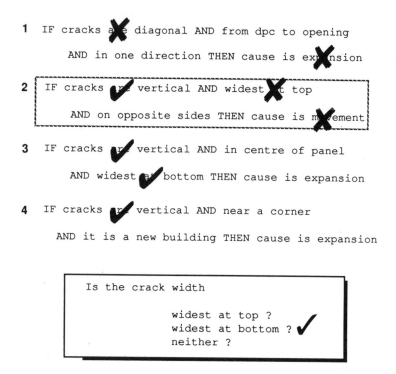

Fig. 1.5 — Second question, answer and consequences.

asked because the system is still evaluating Rule 2 and is now determining whether the second proposition is true. We have chosen an answer to make it not true, hence the current rule (number 2) is cancelled. The system has now exhausted all rules about ground movement and looks for rules (not yet cancelled) about 'expansion'. It finds rule 3 and determines that the first proposition has been evaluated whilst the second has not. Fig. 1.6 shows the question and the answer, which makes the proposition true. Since the third proposition is already true, the system has proved that, for this consultation, rule 3 is true. The conclusion that the likely cause of the cracks is the expansion of the bricks would then be displayed to the user. If we had not given the answer shown in Fig. 1.6, the system would have failed to find a solution and displayed a message to that effect — hardly surprising for a knowledge base of only four rules.

It is an excellent self-learning challenge to trace through a set of rules and determine the sequence of questions and answers which will lead to proving the truth of a selected rule. This forms part of the technique of testing a system. The reader

1   IF cracks are diagonal AND from dpc to opening

AND in one direction THEN cause is expansion

2   IF cracks are vertical AND widest at top

AND on opposite sides THEN cause is movement

3   IF cracks are vertical AND in centre of panel

AND widest at bottom THEN cause is expansion

4   IF cracks are vertical AND near a corner

AND it is a new building THEN cause is expansion

```
Is the crack

        in the centre of the panel ?  ✓
        near a corner ?
        neither ?
```

```
The conclusion is that
    the likely cause is expansion
```

Fig. 1.6 — Third question, answer and conclusion.

might like to find the sequence which causes the last rule of Fig. 1.3 to be true, still starting with movement as the first goal of the search.†

There are many search methods used but all hinge on two features shown by this method which further distinguish expert systems from conventional programs. Firstly, when the system refers to an object which has not been evaluated, it does not stop as an ordinary program would if it tried to use a variable with no value. It sets about finding a value from the necessary rules and questions. Secondly, having obtained a value, an expert system uses it as fully as possible by evaluating *all* propositions that use that object, not just the one that was being investigated. Some search methods go further and chase through all consequent actions, and we shall discuss the merits of some of these in Part II.

To spread these effects through a knowledge base all search methods look for common usage of objects in the rules and create a network of cross-connections

† [Ans. vertical, neither, near corner, new]

between rules and objects, sub-goals or goals. It is in the creation and use of this network of connections that expert systems provide a new way of accessing stored knowledge with their own advantages over the indexes and cross-references we use in books. In a substantial knowledge base of hundreds of rules, the network becomes an unimaginable spider's web, always ensuring that all consequences of an answer to a question are properly acted upon. Whatever searching method is adopted becomes a matter of efficiency in using the connection network to come to a conclusion about a problem rapidly. We see in Chapter 4 how, for efficiency, the searching methods select from the spider's web the 'tree' of interconnections growing from a single goal object. Some shells allow an option of using forward chaining only, and this is more efficient for systems which start with a set of data items and draw conclusions from them. Some applications of data interpretation are described in section 3.4 but we shall not consider them elsewhere in this book.

There are consequences of searching worth drawing attention to. The first is that the rules may clearly be in any order in the knowledge base; the search process will find the next rule to process no matter where it is. That frees the programmer creating the knowledge base from much responsibility when entering rules into the knowledge base, but immediately opens the door to the risk of incomprehensibility creeping in by careless separation of rules that might be better understood if grouped together. A large knowledge base can rapidly become as incomprehensible as a bad BASIC program if care is not taken.

The second direct consequence is more serious and quite fundamental to the appreciation of what expert systems can do. The search process can only find goals that exist in the knowledge base. In other words, it can only find pre-determined solutions to a problem. If the creators of an expert system have not coded knowledge about a possible cause, the computer will not then know anything about it. It is true that artificial intelligence researchers have developed systems capable of generating automatically some knowledge about certain clearly defined and modest problem areas, but it seems unlikely that this will occur in practical engineering applications.

1.4 GIVING THE USER AN EXPLANATION

The third of our key features is the hardest to achieve. To insist that explanations of how an answer was arrived at should be based on the actual knowledge statements used to derive the answer is a fierce demand but ensures that the user can see and understand, and perhaps argue with, the knowledge that has led to a result. Alternatives in the form of potted explanations added to the knowledge base specifically for this purpose are used and have some merits, but the real risk of them not being updated as knowledge statements are amended or added is a crushing disadvantage. We shall look at this idea later in this section.

The questions a user might ask about a conclusion are legion — shells usually allow 'How was this result arrived at?' and 'Why is this question being asked?'. A much neglected question is 'Why was this result found to be not true?', sometimes as useful as knowing what was true. Each explanation is found by the expert system keeping a track of the sequence of rules processed and found true. For the simple four rule set in the preceding section, the answer to 'How was the result of Fig. 1.6 found?' is simply a presentation of rule number 3. Shells vary greatly in their presentation of explanations by wrapping up the rule in various texts to aid legibility, some adopting the first person with alarming overtones. A presentation could be

> the conclusion that
> the likely cause is the expansion of the bricks
> was arrived at from the rule
> 'If direction of the cracks is vertical
> and the cracks are in the centre of a panel
> and the cracks are widest at the bottom
> then the likely cause is expansion of the bricks'.

Clearly the comprehensibility of this explanation hinges upon the near English form of knowledge representation to start with, although a great deal can be done by judicious insertion in the display of appropriate extra words. In a real knowledge base of hundreds of rules, the explanation will be based on a series of rules linked in a hierarchy created by sub-goals as introduced in the last example rule in section 1.2. Rather than attempt to combine these into one explanation, it is usual to display one rule at a time and to provide the user with a means of tracking back as wished through the expanding tree of rules all involved in the result. One method is to allow the user to select an antecedent of the displayed rule, whereupon the system will display the rule or question which led to the value of that antecedent. Fig. 1.7 illustrates the two screens which might be generated from our only example so far of two linked rules.

The answer to 'Why is this question being asked?' is based upon the current rule being processed and the links back to related rules and propositions which have already been proved true. The question could be asked at any stage in the processing of the current rule; hence it becomes necessary to highlight the antecedent which is being evaluated. Thus, before answering the question in Fig. 1.5, the result of 'Why' could be presented as

> to determine whether
> the likely cause is movement of the ground
> from the rule
> 'If the direction of the cracks is vertical
> and the cracks are widest at the top
> and there is a single crack on opposite sides of the building
> then the likely cause is movement of the ground'
> it is necessary to know whether
> the cracks are widest at the top.

As before a linked hierarchy of rules poses a display problem usually solved in the same way but, since we are at an intermediate stage, some antecedents will not yet have been evaluated and the display will have to present that fact appropriately.

The reader may be wondering how a consultation can be interrupted to ask 'How' or 'Why' whilst the expert system is actually asking a question about the problem. Shells provide different solutions to this — using function keys on the keyboard or special characters to be input or special words on the screen to be picked up by a cursor. All allow the consultation to continue at the real question once the user's curiosity is satisfied. Whilst dealing with this operational matter, it is appropriate to

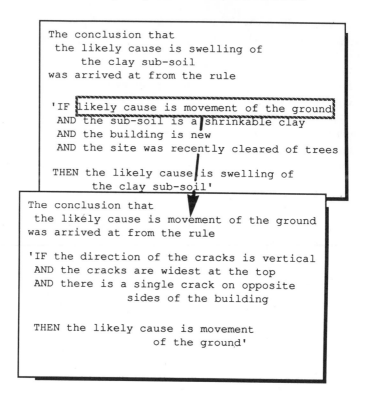

```
The conclusion that
  the likely cause is swelling of
      the clay sub-soil
was arrived at from the rule

 'IF likely cause is movement of the ground
  AND the sub-soil is a shrinkable clay
  AND the building is new
  AND the site was recently cleared of trees

  THEN the likely cause is swelling of
        the clay sub-soil'
```

```
The conclusion that
  the likely cause is movement of the ground
was arrived at from the rule

'IF the direction of the cracks is vertical
 AND the cracks are widest at the top
 AND there is a single crack on opposite
                  sides of the building

  THEN the likely cause is movement
                  of the ground'
```

Fig. 1.7 — Explanation from two linked rules.

mention that some shells also provide a facility to allow users to backtrack through past answers to make changes if needed — a very useful extra.

It is the author's experience that users are also inclined to ask 'Why not?', i.e. why was a possible solution discarded? In an expert system for the diagnosis of the cause of dampness in a building, to be described in Chapter 3, fifteen possible causes are considered. The first version of the system merely informed users by a brief display as causes were dismissed. Their reaction was invariably 'Why was that?' and a way had to be found to satisfy this need. Having done so, it was clear that it helped users considerably to be told, for example, that a problem was *not* due to rising damp. By dismissing in a justified manner an idea that may have been dominant in a user's mind, other possible causes were considered more receptively.

If this facility is to be provided, the first step is to ensure that the expert system evaluates all goals even when one is found to be true. The difficulty then is in offering to a user all goals that have proved to be not true, together with a facility to examine all the related rules that led to the failed goals. There will be many. In contrast to answering 'How was a result arrived at?', where only one rule had to be presented, we must now look at all the rules tried before each goal was abandoned. For example, in our small knowledge base for cracks in walls, three out of the four rules concern expansion. If expansion had been proved to be not true, each rule would need to be presented with the answers to the antecedents (not necessarily all antecedents) which caused the rule to fail. All this is possible but not easy. We shall discuss in Part II the possibility of rules specifically included to help answer this question.

Including extra text in the knowledge base for display as potted explanations, is a solution to this and other problems. As suggested earlier there are merits in this idea but it must be said again that duplicating the knowledge that is in the rules by additional text, creates a major problem for the developer of ensuring that the two remain in step. That said, the advantage is that the text can be made crisp and, in particular, the answers to 'How?', 'Why?' and 'Why not?' can place emphasis on the important pieces of evidence and play down the lesser items in a way that the automatic generation of explanation cannot. Such text also overcomes the somewhat stilted and verbose style of the automatic explanations as illustrated above.

Extra text is well worthwhile including to help users answer the questions. This is hardly 'explanation' but is so very valuable that it is mentioned now. Typically described as 'amplification text' or 'expansion', most shells allow appropriate text to be associated with a question and provide the user with a simple facility to display that text when needed. In the formal task of eliciting knowledge about a specialist field, it is often overlooked that much of an expert's knowledge is in knowing the right answers to give to a question. Amplification text can be used to present that knowledge to a user just as he is trying to answer a question. Chapter 5 in Part II enlarges on this.

1.5 THREE STAGES OF AN EXPERT SYSTEM

So far, this introduction to expert systems has concentrated on the knowledge base and its processing. We look now at an important refinement. We have seen that the searching method allows the rules to be in any order, but the order chosen does have an effect on the user. It determines the sequence in which the questions are put. Strictly, the factors which determine this are:

(a) the order in which the *goals* are searched,
(b) the order in which the *rules* with the same consequent appear, and
(c) the order of the *antecedents* in the rules.

One glance at the small rule set of Fig. 1.3 will make this clear. Imagine that all the rules ended instead of beginning with the propositions about the directions of the cracks. Consultations would then start with quite a different question.

In large knowledge bases, leaving the question sequence entirely to the result of the searching method can easily lead to a rather random set of questions, skipping from one line of query to another. It would be like visiting your doctor and facing questions about your toes, knees, elbows, eyes, head, etc. until he came to the part that hurt!

A real expert would not start a consultation that way and it is worth considering the stages he would go through and how these should be mirrored in an expert system. This is a neglected aspect of expert system development, and Chapter 5 will expand on this. There are, perhaps, three stages to a real consultation — asking preliminary questions; considering the evidence; and making a report. Let us look briefly at them.

(1)   Preliminary questions
We expect an expert to start by asking some basic questions about our problem, and we would be reassured by an expert system which did the same. But an expert does not ask questions in a vacuum. He helps us if we find the question difficult to answer; he will mentally check our answers to see if they are consistent; he will warn us or reject an answer if it seems unlikely or plainly impossible.

(2)   Considering the evidence
The answers to the preliminary questions will suggest a sequence in which to consider the possible solutions. The expert will not use the same fixed sequence for each consultation, but differing sequences appropriate to each problem.

(3)   Making a report
A report may not be delivered until the end of the consultation, but the human expert will certainly have been making mental and real notes throughout his consideration of the problem. Furthermore, the order in which the report is presented will not necessarily be that in which the notes were taken. He will choose an order which will ensure that the client can most easily understand how the conclusion was reached from the evidence (Hercule Poirot's summing up is never in the order of the clues as given).

It seems that some expert systems are just knowledge bases, with little control exerted over the order of the preliminary questions. The author contends that all three stages set out above should be mimicked. The facility to help users answer questions by offering further 'amplification' text has been mentioned in section 1.4 above. This should be used. To go further and to add rules which will check the validity of the answers is quite simple. Changing the order in which the goals of an expert system are processed according to some of or all the answers to the preliminary questions is possible with many shells. Creating a meaningful report for the user is certainly difficult but again possible. An expert system with this overall form would be worthy of the title 'user friendly'. These considerations seem neglected or, at least, overlooked by those developing expert systems. The whole of Chapter 5 is devoted to considering this topic in more detail and giving some examples.

1.6   EXPERT SYSTEMS ARE ADVISERS

Although the point has been made already in section 1.3, it is important in an introduction to the subject to emphasize that expert systems can only search for and display those pre-defined solutions embodied in a knowledge base as goals. If it is a diagnosis system — the goals will be the causes of failure. If it is an advice system — the goals will be all possible pieces of advice. Once started on its searching process, an expert system will home in upon one or more goals proved true by its evaluation of the rules.

We cannot describe this process as anything other than a pale simulation of a human expert's reasoning power. Yes, a large knowledge base of hundreds of rules with scores of goals can make an expert system look remarkably intelligent. Yes, it is possible that a final recommendation is a combination built from several goals, and that multiplies the possibilities enormously. But expert systems are, in the end, entirely predictable, at least at this stage in their development. (Michie & Johnston (1984) present a very readable account of some more imaginative applications of artificial intelligence which readers might find interesting.)

Having said that, there is a place in the construction industry for systems which might better be described as 'advisers' — advisers which, unlike human experts, are always available; which are reliable; which work as well on Monday morning and Friday afternoon as any other time in the week; and which can be consulted privately in the corner of the office without the risk of personal embarrassment due to ignorance. The human equivalent of an expert system is probably that little, bald-headed chap in bottle-end glasses who goes on and on and, worst of all, is always right! But there is a place for expert systems like him. If we can keep them in perspective and start developing knowledge bases with the same care we devote to codes of practice, expert systems have a very real place in an industry which depends so much on experiential knowledge.

1.7 A SHORT HISTORY

Research into artificial intelligence started in the late 1950s but expert systems did not appear until the mid 1970s. A medical system, MYCIN, by Shortliffe (1976), is often cited as the first, and certainly was a major contribution to general awareness of the topic. Similarly, the mineral exploration system, PROSPECTOR, illustrated the potential of the technique in engineering. In construction industry usage, two early contributors can be identified. Bijl *et al.* (1979) showed the use of declarative programming in architectural CAD work, and Lansdown (1982), also an architect, introduced many people to the topic through an RIBA financed report on 'Expert Systems in the Construction Industry'. Others have followed and some references are given later, particularly for the applications described in Chapter 3.

It is perhaps appropriate to end this introductory chapter by comparing the current stage of expert system development with the well-charted history of two classes of programs now accepted by the construction industry. Finite element stress analysis programs were first developed in aircraft stress offices in the mid 1950s leading to much university-based research in the 1960s and a general acceptance of the tool by mid 1970s. Similarly, computer aided drawing systems grew from a few university laboratories with the necessary equipment in the mid 1960s and were accepted in the early 1980s. If this gestation period of approximately 20 years is repeated for expert systems, it will be the mid 1990s before they too become accepted tools. That could well be the case but, as with finite elements and CAD, it will be the organizations that get involved in the development work that first gain the competitive advantage from using them. Bearing in mind that knowledge is a commercial asset, it could also be that, contrary to the two previous examples, expert systems developed by the pioneers will not come on to the market. That behoves all to get to know and use this technology.

2

How to create an expert system

In this chapter, we shall go through the stages of creating an expert system, introducing the basic ideas of each stage in a general discussion, then applying them to a simple example. We shall 'interview' an expert, analyse the knowledge we gain, represent it in rules and then test the resulting system. As before, we shall eschew all complications and qualifications attached to these tasks and leave their discussion to Part II. We shall assume that the knowledge lies in the head of a respected expert and that our overall objective is to ensure that he understands the resulting knowledge base well enough to claim it as his own and to relegate us (retrospectively) to being merely the midwife.

2.1 DO YOU NEED AN EXPERT SYSTEM?

Before starting, it is as well to define the scope of the proposed system and to determine if it is an appropriate problem for this technology. We now have an increasing range of computing methods available to us for problem solving: conventional programming languages, data base programs, spread sheets and now expert system shells. The ideas already set out in Chapter 1 lead to the following guidelines which will be amplified by the description of some actual applications to follow in Chapter 3.

The over-riding characteristic to look for is whether the problem solving method is essentially sequential or not. Are there a clear set of steps which follow one from another with, possibly, a few decision stages which cause some steps to be skipped over? This is common in heavily arithmetical methods, and not uncommon in straightforward data-processing involving, for example, accounts, project records or project management. For these problems, conventional programming languages or spread sheets are likely to be the appropriate technology. If, instead of a definite sequence, the problem solving method involves the simultaneous consideration of many alternative solutions, any one of which may be the answer, then data bases or expert systems are likely to be the right choice. It may help to think of the steps involved and compare them with the idealized diagrams of Fig. 1.2. Even if your proposed problem solving method has the characteristics of the right-hand diagram, it may still be worth considering a data base solution. This will be appropriate if the potential answers all have a similar form and the selection depends only upon a small and fixed set of key parameters, for example when selecting addresses of building merchants in a certain region of the country and specializing in supplying certain components. If the potential solutions depend upon not only some key parameters but also upon extra data items which must satisfy relationships unique to each solution, then an expert system will be called for.

One apparently appropriate application of expert systems, often proposed, is that of helping users follow a code of practice. It is not clear that this is in fact always a suitable application. Codes are generally set out as step-by-step procedures with a few decisions on the way: a recipe for using conventional programming. Where codes offer a wide variety of rules for classification of components or situations, e.g. the classification of occupancy and access in fire codes, an expert system could be the right approach.

2.1.1 An example

The example we shall use in this chapter is that of developing a system to help site engineers to classify soil samples taken from a borehole. The potential solutions will be simply the descriptions such as 'gravel, sand, silt', etc., commonly used to define soils. The solution method will be to ask a few questions about a particle size and cohesion and then to consider all possible classifications, some of which will need more detail to verify or disprove them. There is no element of a step-by-step sequence and the obvious technologies are either a data base or an expert system. A data base solution would not be appropriate because of the varying number of data items needed to confirm some of the classifications and the relationships between these, which we will see expressed as rules appropriate to each classification. We conclude that this problem is suitable for an expert system.

Clearly the decision must then be formalized by defining the scope of the system, but this can form the first step in the most challenging stage — that of eliciting the knowledge from the expert.

2.2 STEP 1 — KNOWLEDGE ELICITATION

It is often claimed that experts think they are very good at describing their solution methods, but only moderately good at actually solving problems, whereas, in reality, they are excellent at solving problems and often appallingly bad at describing how they do it. Whether that generalization is true or not it serves to introduce what is generally held to be the most difficult stage in creating an expert system — that of extracting the knowledge from an expert's head. It is, of course, a problem of communication between people with all the problems of personal relationships, motivation and misunderstandings that dog even our simplest conversations. With the gross simplifications we are allowing ourselves in Part I, we consider this task under three headings:

(a) motivation of the expert,
(b) interviewer's background and style, and
(c) a method

and we relegate to Part II more detailed discussions of these aspects, plus problems of multiple experts, interviewing and recording methods, and the use of computers to assist in this work.

2.2.1 Motivation

The enthusiasm of the expert for the project may be the most important key to its success. Ensuring that this enthusiasm is not skin deep and merely reflects an order from 'above' is, therefore, worthwhile confirming. It is certainly not the author's experience that experts are reluctant to divulge their knowledge, and two simple points may be made to encourage them. Firstly, the expert system when developed will only handle the straightforward problems that probably represent 90% of their work, but work that is rather boring. Release from this chore to create time for the really difficult and interesting problems is a motivation seen several times already. Secondly, impending retirement with a natural pride in trying to preserve a life-time's experience for others, can be another strong motivator. There are others — at this stage it is simply suggested that an indirect assessment of the expert's true commitment be made and be considered.

2.2.2 Interviewer's background and style

Some writers on expert systems have argued that the best type of interviewer ('knowledge engineer' to simply mention the pretentious jargon) is a person with no experience of the proposed topic. The virtue of starting with a completely untrained mind is seen as ensuring that no steps are skipped over by the expert during his description. A corresponding disadvantage is the need by the interviewer to learn all the relevant basics as well as the specialized expertise that will form the knowledge base. At the least, this will consume more of the scarce interviewing time of the expert but also puts on the interviewer the burden of learning far more. The author believes strongly that the interviewer should have an appropriate general back-ground to understand most of the terms used, but be humble enough to ask the simplest of questions if in any doubt. In either case, it is well to recognize the risk of misunderstandings and to overcome these by ensuring that the expert can truly understand 'his' knowledge base.

Apart from having an appropriate background, good communication will only follow if a good 'chemistry' develops between expert and interviewer. It might appear false to adopt the salesman's bible — 'How to make friends and influence people' — but success in developing a happy, friendly relationship will make it easier to backtrack over old ground or to ask apparently stupid questions. All experts do have the problem of remembering how very ignorant the rest of us are on their subject and are given to brief answers and long silences as they assume that we know what they are talking about. A distant and frosty relationship will not help fill those gaps, and it is right to pander to the expert and listen patiently to his long-winded diatribes on side issues in order to build a closer relationship. You might easily learn some relevant fact in any case.

2.2.3   A method
The following steps are recommended:

(a) unstructured interviews,
(b) focused interviews,
(c) case studies, and
(d) prototype demonstrations.

We merely note here that the interviews need to be recorded and that the knowledge will gush out at an alarming rate at infrequent intervals. Methods to handle this without stopping the expert are important and appear in Part II, Chapter 6.

Unstructured interviews are meant to allow the expert to talk generally about the whole problem area. He should be encouraged to describe his problem solving process in general terms, even though the interviewer must be alert to the likelihood of some rambling diversions. The objectives of these discussions should, of course, include that of the interviewer getting some idea of the knowledge used but, more particularly, to define the basic questions the expert would put to a client at the start of a consultation and the range of possible solutions he would consider at the end. These two features start to define the scope of the system. The 'boundary' of the problem will be understood even if the 'inside' is yet to be explored. Of the two high-lighted objectives — the preliminary questions and the possible solutions — the second is the most important and should be considered as the basic objective of the unstructured interviews. Once the solutions are identified and listed, the goals of the expert system are therefore defined, and this sets the scope and the scale of the system. If there is pressure to create the expert system quickly, it would be appropriate to freeze the list of goals at an early stage to help ensure the project is completed on time.

The focused interviews follow and concentrate on each solution, i.e. goal, in turn. The ideal is to ask the expert to work backwards from the goal, through any intermediate steps and so to the detailed questions and relationships needed to confirm that the goal is the solution to a particular problem. This is very difficult to do. Some experts can manage it; others not. It is, of course, the way the expert system will backward chain as it strives to solve a problem, but it is also opposite to the way the expert appears to solve a problem. He may well think in a manner similar to the searching of an expert system, but it will be so fast and instinctive as to appear to lead only to a series of questions. Some experts find it very difficult to describe their knowledge other than by talking their way through the series of questions that are appropriate to a particular problem. IT IS IMPORTANT to recognize whether your expert can discuss his knowledge in an abstract manner working backwards from each goal or prefers to talk through actual problems.

During these focused discussions, the interviewer should also help the expert to identify any key questions which are involved in most, if not all, of the goals. These can be properly identified as preliminary questions, the sort that we would expect an expert to ask at the beginning of a consultation. For example, in a system to diagnose dampness in buildings, which will be described in Chapter 3, the preliminary questions include, 'What sort of building has the damp problem?; how old is it?; where does the dampness occur?'. Most diagnosis or advice expert systems will have such preliminary questions, and identifying them leads to friendly and efficient systems. Because of their key role, it is important to press the expert into providing help for a naive user when answering them. This help can be simply an amplification of the question or can be a display of typical values of a requested data item for practical problems. This help information will be coded into the expert system.

Case studies are very helpful even if the expert has set out his knowledge in the ideal backwards fashion. Records of past problems may not have been kept in exemplary form, but anything will be of some value. At the least, case studies can serve as a useful prompt to re-vitalize an otherwise forgotten experience. If sufficiently detailed, they can provide good test data and, where there is an abundance of case studies, some might be set aside for comparative trials.

The whole process of knowledge elicitation is not a sequence of isolated steps, and the interviewer must expect to go over some or all of the ground several times. By demonstrating an early version of the actual system, the expert can be more easily motivated to such reviews. There are dangers to this however. Exposure to a too simple version can disappoint and de-motivate the expert. Unless he is involved in the coding of the system from the very beginning, it is advisable to wait until it has knowledge about most of the goals before risking a demonstration. Another disadvantage is that the running of an expert system shows only one of possibly thousands of routes through the knowledge. It is valuable to show the expert how the questions appear on the screen and how the help information is presented, but it is wrong to try to confirm the correctness of the knowledge at this stage by a few demonstration runs. The expert must be encouraged to read the knowledge base and to confirm it in that form.

2.2.4 The borehole problem

We have been fortunate enough to locate and get an introduction to Professor Borehole, an aged academic near retirement, specializing in classifying soils and known to be motivated by the chance of immortality. We have arranged to interview him and have carefully looked up some of his past papers so as to get our relationship off to a good start. We go along at the appointed time and allow him to make the obligatory jokes about 'all this new-fangled computer stuff' before complimenting him on his wide range of published papers. And so, having established the right 'chemistry' and being sure of his motivation, we start with the unstructured interview stage.

'Professor Borehole, I wonder if you would start by describing the basis of soil classification.'

'Certainly — we use the general classification of
  very coarse soil
  coarse soil
  fine soil
  organic soil'.

Long silence from Professor B. — you realize he is waiting for you.

'And how do we decide in which class a soil sample falls?'

Professor B., 'We use the particle size for the first three, but not the last, thus —
    very coarse soils, greater than 60 mm particle size
    coarse soils, 60 mm–0.06 mm particle size
    fine soils, less than 0.06 mm'.

'I see - that raises two questions: can we see particles as small as 0.06 mm and how do we classify organic soils?'

Professor B., 'Oh yes, we can see perhaps all the way down to 0.02 mm. As for organic soils, well these include peat which, as you know, is predominantly plant remains, dark in colour, often smelly with low bulk density, and we must also include organic silts, organic clays and organic sands, which are only partly peat.'

Oh dear, I hope I've got all that down in my notebook and now he's finally mentioned clay, silt and sand, which I had expected to hear about to start with. Perhaps it would be better to try to get some definition of these and then do some tidying up.

'Professor Borehole, you've just mentioned clay, silt and sand — could you give me definitions of those.'

'Certainly
    Clay — a fine soil, not possible to distinguish separate particles, smooth, sticks to fingers and dries slowly.
    Silt — a fine soil, coarser than clay, can sometimes see individual particles, also sticks to fingers but dries much more quickly.
    Sands — separate particles are quite easily seen and there is no cohesion when dry.'

That's better, let's make a table in order of size followed by the organic soils.

GENERAL	SIZE (mm)	REFINED CLASSIFICATION
Very coarse	*>60*	*?*
Coarse	*60–0.06*	*Sand*
Fine	*<0.06*	*Silt or Clay*
Organic	*?*	*Peat, Organic Clay, Silt or Sand*

Very worried about fitting organic soils into the system at the moment but we'll leave that until later. I wonder if very coarse soils have more refined classification.

'Is there a more refined classification that we could add for the very coarse soils?'

'Yes, boulders have particle sizes greater than 200 mm but you will not get those in a borehole sample.
Cobbles have particle sizes 60–200 mm, occasionally found in cores but very difficult to recover.'

Good, now what was that reference to tests to help separate clays from silts?

'Are there some simple tests that can be made to help distinguish clays from silts?'

'Yes, you can do a liquid limit test to determine plasticity — silts have low plasticity and clays have high plasticity. You will be able to find out how to do liquid limit tests from any standard textbook on soil mechanics.'

Now all that remains is to handle these awkward organic soils.

'Can we classify organic clays and silts by the same means if the organic material is removed or ignored?'

'Yes.'

Oh, good — that seems to suggest that our expert system rules for clay, silt and sand can be used twice over — once on their own and again in conjunction with the presence of organic material. Well, that seems to be that — a new table to summarize our knowledge and then I can get down to writing some rules.

GENERAL	SIZE (mm)	REFINED CLASSIFICATION	TESTS
Very coarse	>60	Boulders, cobbles	—
Coarse soils	60–0.06	Sand	—
Fine soils	<0.06	Silt, clay	Liquid limit
Organic soils		Peat, organic clays, silt and sand	—

Professor Borehole, 'Well, aren't you going to ask me about gravels?'

Oh, no! Why didn't you mention them yourself, you beep beep professor?

'Of course, I was just about to!'

Professor B., with twinkle in eye, 'Well we are unlikely to have a sand with particles as large as 60 mm, are we?'

Suitably humble 'Quite.'

'Gravels are soils where particles are easily visible to the naked eye. They are sub-divided as follows:

> coarse gravels, 20–60 mm
> medium gravels, 6–20 mm
> fine gravels, 2–6 mm.'

'So gravels cover the larger particle sizes in our 'coarse soil' classification, presumably leaving sand to describe the smaller particle sizes in that group. Does that mean that sands are also sub-divided?'

'Yes.

> coarse sands, 0.6–2 mm
> medium sands, 0.2–0.6 mm
> fine sands, 0.06–0.2 mm'

We seem to be going backwards rapidly here. Does this mean that silts and clays are also sub-divided?

'Are silts and clays also sub-divided by particle size?'

Professor Borehole, 'Clays, no; silts, yes, as follows:

> coarse silts, 0.02–0.06 mm
> medium silts, 0.006–0.02 mm
> fine silts, 0.002–0.006 mm.'

'But I thought you said that we could distinguish particle sizes down to 0.06 mm only.'

'Yes, you would need to use a measuring microscope to distinguish medium and fine silts.'

Better be very humble now.

'If we draw up a new table, will that complete the knowledge for soil classification?'

Professor Borehole, with another twinkle in his eye, 'Yes — you have just about got the first four columns of Table 6 in BS 5930.' (See Table 2.1).

This was, of course, an artificial interview, but it is hoped that it illustrated some of the difficulties. The unstructured interview merged into the focused interview, the expert needed prodding, particularly at the start, the knowledge came out in fits and starts, and the expert quite overlooked the fact that the interviewer did not know about the divisions of sand and gravel according to particle size.

2.3   STEP 2 — ANALYSING AND REPRESENTING THE RESULTS OF THE KNOWLEDGE ELICITATION

Do not expect or attempt to immediately code the knowledge you elicited into an expert system shell. As with the writing of a conventional program, it pays to analyse the problem and do some preparatory work off the computer. The first two steps have been highlighted already as the principal objectives of the knowledge elicitation stage — identifying the *goals* and the *preliminary questions*. However, in even the smallest and simplest problems, there are usually intermediate steps in the thinking process that lead from the preliminary questions to the correct goal. Identifying these as sub-goals is an important step in this analysis. As an example, in the description of the dampness diagnosis system in Chapter 3, Fig. 3.1 shows that the goal of damp due to pipe-leakage has four sub-goals of leaking pipes in different locations such as floor, walls, ceiling and loft and, in each case, a further subdivision according to whether the leakage is from a supply pipe or a drainage pipe.

The next stage is that of formulating the text of the preliminary questions to be put to the user — although the following comments apply also to the detailed questions that arise in only a few rules. There are several points to be borne in mind when considering both the question and the possible answers.

Table 2.1 — Extract from Table 6: BS 5930 Site Investigation.

	Basic soil type	Particle size, mm	Visual identification	Particle nature and plasticity
Very coarse soils	BOULDERS		Only seen complete in pits or exposures	Particle shape:
		— 200		
	COBBLES		Often difficult to recover from boreholes.	Angular
		— 60		Subangular
Coarse soils (over 65% sand and gravel sizes)	GRAVELS	coarse — 20 medium — 6 fine — 2	Easily visible to naked eye; particle shape can be described; grading can be described. Well graded: wide range of grain sizes, well distributed. Poorly graded: not well graded. (May be uniform: size of most particles lies between narrow limits; or gap graded: an intermediate size of particle is markedly under-represented.)	Subrounded Rounded Flat Elongate Texture:
	SANDS	coarse — 0.6 medium — 0.2 fine — 0.06	Visible to naked eye; very little or no cohesion when dry; grading can be described. Well graded: wide range of grain sizes, well distributed. Poorly graded: not well graded. (May be uniform: size of most particles lies between narrow limits; or gap graded: an intermediate size of particle is markedly under-represented.)	Rough Smooth Polished
Fine soils (over 35% silt and clay sizes)	SILTS	coarse — 0.02 medium — 0.006 fine — 0.002	Only coarse silt barely visible to naked eye; exhibits little plasticity and marked dilatancy; slightly granular or silky to the touch. Distintegrates in water; lumps dry quickly; possess cohesion but can be powdered easily between fingers.	Non-plastic or low plasticity
	CLAYS		Dry lumps can be broken but not powdered between the fingers; they also disintegrate under water but more slowly than silt; smooth to the touch; exhibits plasticity but no dilatancy; sticks to the fingers and dries slowly; shrinks appreciable on drying usually showing cracks. Intermediate and high plasticity clays show these properties to a moderate and high degree, respectively.	Intermediate plasticity (Lean clay) High plasticity (Fat clay)
Organic soils	ORGANIC CLAY, SILT or SAND	Varies	Contains substantial amounts of organic vegetable matter.	
	PEATS	Varies	Predominantly plant remains usually dark brown or black in colour, often with distinctive smell; low bulk density.	

Extracts from BS 5930 1981 are reproduced by permission of BSI. Complete copies can be obtained from BSI at Linford Wood, Milton Keynes, MK14 6LE, UK.

(a) The user must find the question easy to answer.
(b) The answer will appear in the rules which must be easy to understand.
(c) Questions with a 'menu' of answers or a numerical answer contain far more information than questions with a simple yes/no answer.

The first point is obvious, the last may be verified by looking back to the brickwork example of Chapter 1, but the second needs further discussion since it leads to some difficult semantic puzzles. It is necessary to consider three matters simultaneously; (i) the text of the question, (ii) the answer the user can give and (iii) the name of the object in which the answer will be stored since that will appear in the rules. Let us consider in advance a question which will appear in the borehole system. One piece of evidence to help separate clays from silts is the rate at which the soil dries on the finger. We need to formulate a question about this and to anticipate propositions for rules about clays and silts. One solution might be:

'Does the soil dry quickly on the finger?
Yes/no'

If the name of the associated object was quick_drying_soil, the rules would contain propositions such as
IF quick_drying_soil is yes, and
IF quick_drying_soil is no.

(It is a common requirement that names of objects must not use spaces, hence the underscore is used instead to link the words.)
We would not use such phrases in normal conversation, and so they should be avoided. A better solution is

'At what rate does the soil dry on the finger?
Quick
Slow'

with the answer being given to an object called drying_rate_of_soil.

This allows us to write propositions such as
IF drying_rate_of_soil is quick, and
IF drying_rate_of_soil is slow.

The problem of choosing object names and their related texts is key to retaining comprehensibility of the knowledge and will be examined again in Chapter 7.
The analysis has now established enough structure to start constructing rules and the further detailed questions. It is sensible to continue doing this work in the same sequence we have used already — preliminary questions; sub-goals; final goals. For example, there may be rules to help control the preliminary question sequence to avoid asking irrelevant questions. Taking another example from the dampness system, before asking for the age of the building the user is asked if the building has been finished. Clearly, if it has not, the question of age will be pointless and a rule is included to avoid asking the question. Considering such rules for preliminary

questions, then rules for sub-goals and, finally, rules for the concluding goals is a simple and natural reflection of the order of the analysis.

By breaking the chain of reasoning down to small steps, it becomes much easier to formulate appropriate rules. It is timely at this stage to re-emphasize the isolated, watertight nature of each rule, since this feature simplifies the task so much. When analysing the knowledge and formulating a rule, it is only necessary to think about the antecedent objects, their values and the correct logical connectors to define a set of propositions appropriate to the one sub-goal or goal under consideration. It is not necessary to worry about whether the objects in this rule appear in other rules or not — concentrate on defining a comprehensive and correct rule for the current consequent.

As the analysis proceeds, it will be necessary to record the developing ideas so as to enable the knowledge base to be coded into the chosen expert system shell. If the knowledge representation of the shell is clear and comprehensible, this record may be attempted in something approaching the final form, and, if a word-processing program is used, this will allow both the development of the record and its final editing into the form needed by the shell. It is quite helpful to separate the questions and the rules in this record. For the questions, you should record the name of the associated object, the text of the question and the list of possible answers. The rules can then be set out separately and in the form which has already been illustrated.

If the shell that is to be used has a less than comprehensible manner of representing rules, and unfortunately many shells do, it is a useful and common step to write the knowledge base in an intermediate form often called a 'paper' model. This can take the form as just described above and will act as the common ground between expert and shell. Unfortunately, it requires real discipline to keep both the paper model and the real knowledge base in step. The author's already frequently expressed bias towards shells which allow for a comprehensible knowledge base makes this an unnecessary step.

A separate idea for clarifying the analysis corresponds to the notions of flow charts or structure charts for conventional programs. A knowledge diagram can be drawn to show the objects and goals used in the knowledge base and the links between them as created by the rules. This complements, rather than replaces, the knowledge base but can draw to the attention of the expert elements that have been overlooked. A diagram will be illustrated later.

Lastly, a modest warning stemming from experience. It is only too easy as a knowledge base grows, to inadvertently invent the same, or nearly the same, question and object over again. At the least, this could cause the user to be asked the same question twice but, more often, will lead to a faulty knowledge base.

2.3.1 Analysis of the borehole knowledge
As ideas for rules develop during this analysis, we shall record them in the form of the simple shell described in Chapter 4. This allows rules to be written in the style illustrated in Chapter 2 with two extra elements. The word 'are' can be used instead of 'is' to help comprehensibility, and the consequent of a rule may be an action — particularly that of forcing the system to ask a question. Such actions are distinguished by preceding the appropriate command word with an asterisk, e.g. *ASK.

Following the recommendation just given, we first decide upon goals of the system. We could be content with the broad classifications such as gravel, sand, silt, etc., but it would seem to be more helpful to use the refined goals, such as coarse gravel, medium gravel, etc. We accept Professor Borehole's assertion that one can distinguish by the naked eye particles down to approximately 0.02 mm, but draw the line at that. This leaves us with the following set of goals:

> coarse gravel
> medium gravel
> fine gravel
> coarse sand
> medium sand
> fine sand
> coarse silt
> medium/fine silt
> clay
> organic clay
> organic silt
> organic sand
> peat.

The thirteen goals in this list each have one possible answer — 'the correct classification'. It is perfectly possible to replace them by one goal, say 'classification', with thirteen possible answers, e.g. 'coarse gravel', 'medium gravel', etc. The latter appears more obvious but creates many problems by making the order in which solutions are tried and questions are asked depend upon the order in which the rules appear in the knowledge base. Changes, such as adding a new rule, can completely upset the inferencing order. By having thirteen separate goals, control is handled by the action list and the rules can be ordered independently in ways more natural to the expert.

We now consider candidates for the preliminary questions. The most obvious is the size of individual particles. However, since coarse silts have particles 'barely visible to the naked eye' and medium/fine silts and clays have no visible particles, it would be an improvement to ask first a question about the visibility of individual particles. For example,

> 'How would you describe the visibility of separate particles?
> Easily seen
> Just discernible
> Not discernible'.

We will assume that the second answer implies the particle size that occurs in coarse silt and we will only ask for an estimate of the actual size if the first answer is given. This would be triggered off by a rule which has as its consequent a definite action — a form of the rule referred to at the beginning of this section. To put all this together — if the answer to the question about the visibility of separate particles is stored in an object called 'separate_particles', such a rule could be

> IF separate_particles are 'easily seen'
> THEN *ASK particle_size_mm

and the object 'particle_size_ mm' could be associated with the question

'What is your estimate of the average particle size in mm?'

Another obvious preliminary question would be one to determine whether the sample is peat or not, since a positive answer will end the consultation immediately. This suggests that this might be the first preliminary question, preceding those about particle visibility. This would also allow us to distinguish at this stage the organic soils which are only partly peat and when they occur to direct the user to answer the remaining questions by concentrating on the soil part of his sample. This suggests a menu question of the form

'How much organic vegetable material does the soil sample contain?'
None
Substantial
100%'.

There are no other obvious preliminary questions, and this completes the first analysis of the knowledge.

We have considered the start and the end of the consultation and must now look to see if there are any useful intermediate steps or sub-goals. Looking back at Table 2.1, it seems that a broad classification of the sample as sand, silt or clay, can be made simply upon cohesion and the rate at which soil dries on the fingers. A further test, the liquid limit test, is necessary to confirm whether the soil is clay or silt, and the particle size is necessary to determine the class of sand. This suggests that there would be merit in having an intermediate sub-goal called 'soil' taking the values

Sand
Probably silt
Probably clay.

We can use the simple evidence of cohesion and drying rate to select which value is appropriate and then add the refining tests to get the final goals. For example, we could have a rule such as

IF soil is 'probably clay'
AND separate_particles are 'not visible'
AND liquid_limit% > 35
THEN clay is 'the correct classification'.

We can also use this sub-goal in rules for the organic soils since it is probably unnecessary to go to a refined classification for these cases. This suggests rules such as

> IF organic_content is 'substantial'
> AND soil is 'probably silt'
> THEN organic_silt is 'the correct classification'.

It is hardly worthwhile developing a knowledge diagram for this simple system, but since they can be helpful for more complex problems, Fig. 2.1 has been drawn to illustrate one form. The final goals are on the left and the links represent the relationships embodied in rules between the goals, sub-goals and questions. The backward chaining search can be followed by starting from the appropriate goal and working rightwards across the diagram through any sub-goals, if present, until the questions are reached on the righthand side. The order of the questions will be down the page if the diagram accurately reflects the order of the propositions in the rules. One problem of these diagrams can be seen by comparing the upper half, which refers to clays, with the lower half, which refers to silts. Because there are only two clay goals, the sub-goal 'soil' can be nicely positioned between them, leaving a neat diagram. When a sub-goal is used in more than two rules, as for the three silty goals in the lower part of the diagram, this neatness disappears. Dotted lines, which link to a separate little diagram for the sub-goal, are one solution. If the propositions can also be accommodated on the diagram, the whole can be a very compact presentation of an expert's knowledge and, just as a picture can paint a thousand words, so such a diagram can reproduce many pages of rules. They are difficult to draw — it's best to use a CAD package to allow easy updating — but can help an expert to spot missing links or missing sections of knowledge.

2.4 STEP 3 — CODING AND TESTING

Preparing the final knowledge base is best done with a word-processing program, and most shells either build in an equivalent or accept a computer file created by a standard WP program. The details of the final form will, of course, depend upon the intended shell. However, there are usually three elements — the text of the questions with their associated objects, the rules and a list of actions the system is to take, such as the preliminary questions to be asked and the goals to be evaluated in an appropriate order. Fig. 2.2 shows the questions and answers for our borehole system; Fig. 2.3 shows the rules and the action list. Many shells convert the knowledge base from this readable form to a form more suited to fast execution. This is roughly equivalent to the compilation needed by FORTRAN programs but not by BASIC programs. This conversion also provides the opportunity of making checks upon the correctness of the form of the knowledge, for example to make sure that propositions are joined together by correct terms such as AND and OR. A very useful by-product is a list of all the objects found in the rules with a warning if an object appears once only. This can be a useful hint to a mis-typed object name creating an unwanted object.

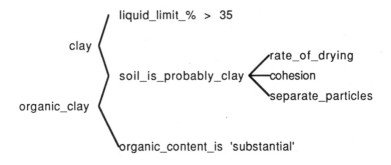

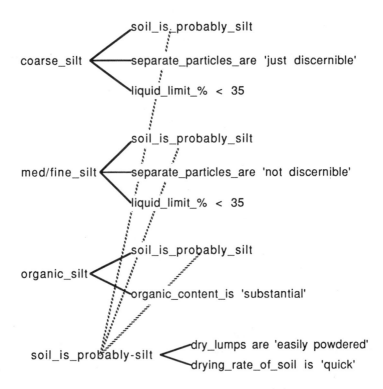

Fig. 2.1 — Knowledge diagram for part of the borehole system.

One cannot pretend that testing and verifying an expert system is an easy task, and this will form the material for later discussion in Chapter 8. The action of the searching process takes away the simple notion of proceeding through rules in a fixed order and, if a mistake is made in a rule by omitting an intended proposition, the embryo expert system can seem to have a mind of its own. A key point to remember is that there are a very large number of possible routes through the system according to the way the user answers the questions. It is essential, therefore, to constrain the system during the testing process by controlling what the system is allowed to search

```
organic_content
How much vegetable material does the soil contain ?
                none
                substantial
                one hundred percent

separate_particles
How would you describe the visibility
        of separate particles ?
                easily seen
                just discernble
                not discernible

particle_size_mm
What is your estimate of the average particle
        size in mm ?

dry_lumps
How would you describe the way a dry lump of soil
        crumbles between the fingers ?
                easily disintegrated
                easily powdered
                broken into smaller lumps

drying_rate_of_soil
What is the rate at which the soil dries
        on the finger ?
                quick
                slow


liquid_limit%
What is the liquid limit in percent ?
```

Fig. 2.2 — Question objects for the borehole system.

for. Those shells which provide a simple means of specifying objects or goals to be investigated are the easiest to work with.

To illustrate this with our borehole system, we know that there are two rules which will be triggered by the preliminary questions — the first two rules in Fig. 2.3. By removing from the action list all but the two objects 'organic_content' and 'separate_particles', the system will be constrained to explore the first two rules only. When they have been tested, it would be sensible to put on to the action list the sub-goal of 'soil'. By extending the list in this step-by-step manner, the scope of the system can be gradually enlarged with each new set of tests building upon confirmed rules. In all this work it is necessary to be quite aware of the searching method your shell uses. Some illustrations of the surprises the different methods can spring will be shown in Chapter 8.

An illustration of a final test run for the borehole system appears in Fig. 2.4. The shortcomings of this simple system will be obvious: it cannot cope with mixtures of

Firstly rules controlling the preliminary questions

```
IF organic_content is 'substantial'
THEN *DISPLAY 'Please answer the remaining questions
by examining the non-organic content of your sample'

IF separate_particles are 'easily seen'
THEN *ASK particle_size_mm
```

Now the rules for the sub-goals

```
IF dry_lumps are 'easily disintegrated'
AND separate_particles are 'easily seen'
THEN soil is 'sand'

IF dry_lumps are 'easily powdered'
AND drying_rate_of_soil is 'quick'
THEN soil is 'probably silt'

IF dry_lumps are 'broken into smaller lumps'
AND drying_rate is 'slow'
AND separate_particles are 'not discernible'
THEN soil is 'probably clay'
```

Some of the   main rules for classification

```
IF particle_size_mm <= 60
AND particle_size > 20
THEN coarse_gravel is 'the correct classification'

IF soil is 'probably silt'
AND separate_particles are 'not discernible'
AND liquid_limit% < 35
THEN medium/fine_silt is'the correct classification'

IF soil is 'probably clay'
AND liquid_limit% >= 35
THEN clay is 'the correct classification'
```

Part of the ACTION list

```
organic_content
separate_particles
clay
medium/fine_silt
coarse_silt
    etc.
```

Fig. 2.3 — Some rules for the borehole system

soils, such as sandy clays; it does not give the user any option about performing the liquid limit test — he must do it!; there is no text provided to help the user answer any of the questions. But it is hoped that it serves not only to introduce the steps of creating an expert system, but also to put into concrete terms the abstract ideas of Chapter 1. It is appropriate to close this chapter by asking the reader to look again at the rules of Fig. 2.3 and to view each rule as an independent, simple and clear

```
How much vegetable material does the soil contain ?
        1   none
        2   substantial
        3   one hundred percent
Select an option
        (1)

How would you describe the visibility
        of separate particles ?
        1   easily seen
        2   just discernble
        3   not discernible
Select an option
        (3)

How would you describe the way a dry lump of soil
        crumbles between the fingers ?
        1   easily disintegrated
        2   easily powdered
        3   broken into smaller lumps
Select an option
        (2)

What is the rate at which the soil dries
        on the finger ?
        1 quick
        2 slow
Select an option
        (1)

What is the liquid limit in percent ?
Input a number between 0 and 100
        (20)

  The conclusion is that
        medium/fine silt is the correct classification
```

▪▪▪

                   User's input is (ringed)

Fig. 2.4 — A consultation of the borehole system.

statement of what characteristics can be expected of a soil sample in each classification. It is the comprehensibility of those rules compared to the incomprehensibility of most programs that is the greatest merit of expert systems.

3

Applications in the construction industry

The objective of this chapter — the last of Part I — is to complete the introduction to expert systems by illustrating some of the applications already being made. It is hoped that this will help 'place' the technology and enable readers to see further applications more easily.

We have focused in this book on the straightforward usage of expert systems in the fields of diagnosis of faults, selections of material and the offering of advice. The latter field is wide and extends easily into two closely related and potentially important areas — that of the interpretation of data and of control. If we add to the list the speculative possibilities of design, we can construct a portfolio of application areas. Since spotting further successful applications in each field hinges upon identifying the goals of the new expert system, the following general classification also indicates what the goals are for each type.

TYPE	GOALS
Diagnosis	faults
Selection	components
Advisory	recommendations
Interpretation of data	recommendations
Monitoring and Control	actions
Design	design suggestions

This list reflects in a sense the difficulty of constructing an expert system — certainly the last is the most difficult and very much a topic of research. However, it should be noted that selection and advisory systems could be very useful 'design assistants' sitting at the elbow of a real designer to help at detail stages. Before describing a representative example in each class and summarizing other applications, the reader should be warned that many so-called expert systems appearing in published papers are nothing more than a re-vamped version of an old and perfectly good conventional program.

3.1 DIAGNOSTIC SYSTEMS

Diagnosis offers a most obvious use of expert systems since the list of possible faults that cause a problem form the natural list of goals for a system. The symptoms which are most likely to be immediately obvious lead naturally to a set of preliminary questions with other detailed questions arising as rules are developed to confirm each fault as a goal.

3.1.1 Diagnosing dampness in buildings — BREDAMP

The author, with his colleagues and with experts from the United Kingdom Building Research Establishment (BRE), has developed an expert system (BREDAMP) to diagnose the causes of dampness in buildings. This has been described elsewhere (Allwood *et al.*, 1988) and will be summarized here. Damp in buildings, from brick-built houses to multi-storey office blocks, is a problem common to all damp climates. The damp will show itself in many ways — stains, mildew, excrescences, lifting of wall or floor coverings, or simply wet patches. The problem of locating the cause is made difficult by the creeping properties of water and the many routes for the water to take through porous materials or along surfaces. An expert from the BRE Technical Advisory Service has identified 15 separate causes of dampness, and these formed the set of goals for the expert system. They are set out in Table 3.1. The

Table 3.1 — The goals of BREDAMP

CONDENSATION	— moisture deposited on cold surfaces
RAIN PENETRATION	— through roofs or walls
BUILT IN WATER	— enclosed in the structure during construction
PIPE LEAKAGE	— from water supply pipes or drains
PIPE CONDENSATION	— moisture deposited on cold pipes
SPILLAGE	— effect of spillages or excess cleaning water
SEEPAGE	— ground water passing into the structure
RISING DAMP	— ground water rising up walls
CHIMNEY DAMP	— brown stains on existing or old chimneys
CONTAMINATED SAND	— sea sand used in mortar or concrete mixes
CALCIUM CHLORIDE	— added for frost protection or for quick setting
COMPOSITION FLOORS	— magnesium oxychlorides broken down to chlorides
INDUSTRIAL CONTAMINATION	— salts from existing or old industrial processes
ANIMAL CONTAMINATION	— salts from animal waste
FLOODING	— consequences of past floods

knowledge elicitation was carried out by interviews, concentrating on one goal at a time. The more complex goals, such as rain penetration, were broken down to sub-goals, such as rain penetration through walls, through roofs of different construction, through windows, etc. The interview notes were analysed and turned into knowledge diagrams drawn on a CAD System. One is illustrated in Fig. 3.1 for the goal 'Pipe — leakage'. By way of explanation, the goal is on the left hand side of the diagram and the rules are on the right. Those objects whose names end with 'Q' are questions to be put to the user, other objects are goals and sub-goals determined by the rules. The links joining the objects represent the rules and other knowledge statements.

It was immediately apparent from the knowledge elicitation that this system had to embody uncertainty in its knowledge, and this is a topic deliberately avoided so far but discussed later in Chapter 9. It is enough to say now that many applications in construction will be founded upon uncertain data and with uncertain conclusions to be drawn from that data — many of our problems cannot be mathematically analysed, and we rely on 'rules of thumb' with their inevitable uncertainty. The dampness expert system was coded for a shell which allows for uncertainty in the knowledge representation. In this approach the consequent of a rule is the probability of a cause being the true cause, and one effect of the design of this expert system was that all goals had to be evaluated, i.e. the probabilities of every cause being the true culprit were determined. The system concludes by displaying the most probable cause and also the probabilities for all causes. The shell used was SAVOIR which will be referenced in Appendix 3.

Upon execution, the system starts by asking a set of preliminary questions about the building. In summary, these are:

> Function of building, e.g. house, office, warehouse
> Age — if construction is finished
> Number of storeys
> Type of roof and angle of pitch
> Where dampness seen and the shape of the stain.

One of these questions illustrates well the detailed nature of an expert's knowledge. Fig. 3.2 shows the nine different options offered to the user when answering the question 'What is the shape of the stain?'. The layman is unlikely to even notice such subtleties as 'crescent shaped', 'semi-circular', etc., yet these are important clues to the expert — it is, of course, just an illustration of why we go to experts.

The dampness expert system provides help to the user when answering these questions by displaying further amplification text as requested. After getting answers to the preliminary questions, the system evaluates the causes in their order of likelihood. Each goal has rules which must be satisfied before its probability is determined from the uncertainty knowledge. These rules are in the rectangular boxes in Fig. 3.1 and express simple facts such as that rising damp will not occur on upper floors. These lead to the early elimination of unlikely causes, and the user is immediately informed when a cause is so eliminated by a display of the knowledge leading to that result. This amounts to an explanation of 'Why not?'. This has proved to be just as interesting to users as the answer to the question 'Why?', when a successful cause has been found.

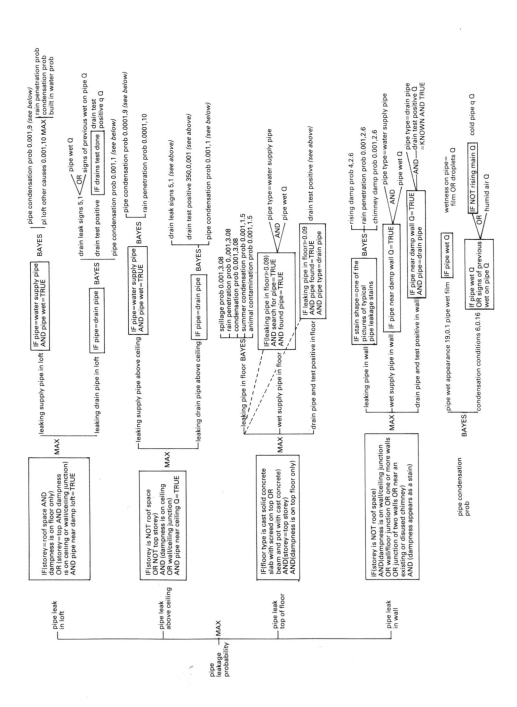

Fig. 3.1 — Knowledge diagram for pipe leakage in BREDAMP.

```
What is the shape of the stain ?


     1. A crescent in the corner of a wall
     2. A horizontal band on a wall
     3. A complete circle
     4. Roughly semi-circular
     4. A three-quarter circle
     6. An irregular patch
     7. A vertical band down a wall
     8. A band across the ceiling
     9. None of these


Enter a number between 1 and 9
```

Fig. 3.2 — Question on stain shape from BREDAMP.

When all goals have been evaluated, the cause with the largest probability is displayed and also the probabilities of all causes. It is common to find two causes with comparable probabilities — this simply reflects the difficulty the expert would have in separating those causes from the evidence provided, but it may still be enough to focus the user's attention on these causes to lead to a firmer conclusion after further investigations.

When answering questions, the user is allowed in many cases to answer 'Don't know'. This option is important if the question concerns, for example, the result of performing a test which would strengthen a conclusion but which is not strictly essential. The distinction between rising damp and condensation may hinge upon determining whether there are salts present in the damp stain — however, a salt test may not be possible. When coding the expert's knowledge, decisions were taken on how an unknown answer should be used to weight the calculation of a probability or whether a suitable and reliable default value could be used as a substitute answer. Allowing 'unknown' as well as 'yes' or 'no' in propositions is discussed in section 9.2.

Some figures describing the system size and effort needed to create it may be helpful. The knowledge elicitation and planning took 30 man days including the time of the expert. The coding and testing took 45 man days. The knowledge base contains approximately 4000 lines of text, much of it for display. There are 143 questions and 171 rules. The system runs on a micro with 512 Kbytes of memory and one floppy disc drive. It takes approximately three seconds between questions to update the knowledge base and to search for the next question when running on an IBM AT.

3.1.2   Other diagnostic systems
An expert system for diagnosing faults in centrifugal pumps has been described by Reinschmidt & Finn (1986). The system is designed for on-site diagnosis by maintenance personnel of problems with pumps in power and process plants. It asks questions to identify the systems, diagnoses the cause and suggests remedies. The user can invoke 'tutorials' to explain terminology and procedures. They also describe

a system for the diagnosis of field welding defects. Over 50 causes of defects are handled, and the system can be used on site by welders or supervisors.

Sharpe & Aldham (1988) report on a prototype system to diagnose faults in the setting up of an electron beam welder. Hamilton & Harrison (1986), in a useful survey, report on two commercially available expert systems for diagnosing faults in building services installations, developed from experience on off-shore oil installations.

3.2 SELECTION SYSTEMS

Much of the skill in detailed design lies in knowing which material or which standard component to use in a particular situation. Expert systems clearly have a place here working as 'design assistants' readily available at all time, unlike the real expert. The goals of such systems will be the set of all possible materials or all available components and, in some cases, combinations of a basic set can build up to a very large library of recommendations. It may be that there is not one solution to each problem, but several, in which case presenting all or a selection to the user with some further data to assist in the final choice may be needed. Cost estimates could be such additional selection factors.

3.2.1 Selection of paint schemes for structural steelwork

The author and a colleague have developed for the Ove Arup Partnership a prototype expert system to select the most suitable paint treatment to protect structural steelwork from corrosion. Such paint schemes consist of a specification for the treatment of the steelwork before painting begins, a primer coat, a barrier coat and a finish which itself may be several coats. A complete scheme will usually include all four components but, in some circumstances, both or either of the barrier and finish layers may be omitted and, in the circumstances of steelwork which is invisible and inside a dry building, it may be correct to do nothing to it at all. At the suggestion of the expert, goals of this system are not complete paint schemes, but are the lists of possible surface treatments, possible primers, possible barriers and possible finishes, each including the component 'Do nothing'. The system asks a set of preliminary questions about the environment, fire protection, target costs, maintenance periods and where the painting is to be done, and then determines by rules which surface treatments, primers, barriers and finishes are suitable. There may be many in each class of component found to be suitable. The system then works through all possible combinations of these goals, taking one surface treatment, one primer, etc., at a time and uses a further set of rules to determine whether each particular combination satisfies other constraints such as chemical compatibility of adjacent layers, compatibility with fire protection coats, ability to resist chemical attack, overall thickness and overall cost. Combinations which satisfy these rules are then sorted into cost order and the cheapest set is displayed to the user.

A particularly interesting feature of this system is that it stops at the stage of having evaluated the suitability or not of each possible component before starting the combination phase. The user sees a set of displays of the answers given to the preliminary questions and the lists of all possible components followed by the word 'suitable' or 'unsuitable'. The user can then examine the rules which led to any of those results to find why a component was rejected or not before proceeding to get the final set of combinations. The LEONARDO shell which was used for this application will be referenced in Appendix 3. One particular feature of the know-ledge representation of this shell not yet introduced in this book is the ability to define a set of goals as belonging to a class. Each goal in a class can be associated with a set of rules and related data which fall into a repeated pattern known as a frame. One frame for the paint selection system is shown in Fig. 3.3 where it will be seen that

```
1:          Name: pickle
2:      Longname: Acid clean (pickle)
3:          Type:
4:         Value:
5:     Certainty:
6: Derivedfrom:
7:Defaultvalue: suitable
8: Queryprompt: never
9:           Isa: surface_treatment
10:       Static:
11.Memberslots:
12:    Shop_cost: 1.0
13:    Site_cost: 100.0
14:    Thickness: 0.0
15: Ease_of_application: 4
16:    compat_with_primer: galv729, galv729_twash
17:    Primer_life_factor: 1.00, 1.00
18:
19:      Ruleset:
20:
21:      IF steelwork_condition is not 'new'
22:      THEN pickle is unsuitable
23:
24:      IF where_surface_prep >= 4
25:      THEN pickle is unsuitable
```

Fig. 3.3 — Frame of knowledge for paint selection system.

this concept concentrates all knowledge relevant to one paint on to one page of paper, making it very easy for the expert to confirm the accuracy of that knowledge, including both rules and data. All the goals belonging to a class can then be processed in a very compact and efficient way by means which will be described generally in Chapter 7.

The statistics for the paint system are that it has approximately 300 rules and runs on a micro with 612 Kbytes and a hard disc. It takes 10/15 minutes for a consultation.

3.2.2 Other selection systems

A selection system reported by Atkinson (1987) chooses the right type of steel for boiler tubes carrying water or steam at high temperature and pressures. The choice is difficult with both code of practice and in-house rules to satisfy, coupled with a trade-off between expensive high-grade material capable of taking high stresses against cheaper material taking lower stresses but, therefore, needing to be made thicker. One advantage noted by Atkinson stemmed from a change in a company rule during the development of the expert system. It was expected that the manual would be out of date for several weeks before a correction was circulated, whereas the expert system was corrected in five minutes.

Cooper (1987) has described an expert system to help planning engineers select the appropriate type of tower crane for use in multi-storey construction. The system incorporates graphics to display a plan of the site and building, together with information about loads to be lifted in various areas on that plan. The user is invited to position the tower of one or more cranes and to define the radius of the jibs. The system then determines automatically what load is to be lifted and searches a data base to find what cranes are possible. After asking questions to determine what material is to be lifted, the system makes an evaluation of the utilization of the cranes over the specified contract period. Advice is then offered to increase or reduce the craneage selected for the job according to the utilization figures obtained. Hamilton & Harrison (1986) report on progress made in developing ACE, a system for the selection of air-conditioning plant.

3.3 ADVISORY SYSTEMS

The goals of an advisory expert system are the pre-defined recommendations to cover as many circumstances as the expert can envisage. It is clearly not as easy to draw up a list of such goals as for the diagnostic and selection systems just described. However, some interesting systems have already been reported, and the following examples, whilst not all from the construction industry, show what possibilities there are.

3.3.1 Advice on strategic planning of construction projects

A set of four advisory expert systems has been developed for the U.K. ALVEY community club formed by the Royal Institute of Chartered Surveyors. These systems offer advice during the strategic planning of a building scheme and have been fully reported by Brandon *et al.* (1988). The four systems, which are integrated by a common data base, offer advice under the following headings:

(a) *Financial budget.* What will be the approximate cost of the sort of building the client wants?
(b) *Procurement.* What will be the most appropriate division of responsibilities between the design and construction teams?
(c) *Time.* How long will it take to design and build?
(d) *Appraisal.* What is the likely profitability of the scheme?

The budget module asks the user approximately 25 preliminary questions concerning the quality, form and size of the proposed building. The expert system, which acts as an 'intelligent front-end' to a conventional estimating model, then uses its 1500 rules to choose basic elements for the building so as to satisfy the user's wishes. From these elements it makes estimates of the cost and prints a summary statement and a 20 page report on the assumptions it has made about the building. A most interesting facility is that of allowing the user to select and change any of 150 key variables and to see the effect the change has had on the final costs. The module has been validated on 40 projects and found to be more reliable than the experts.

The system uses the SAVOIR shell and runs on an IBM compatible PC with a hard disc. It is now being sold to the members of the RICS.

3.3.2 Other advisory systems

Claims by or on contractors are handled by expert systems described by Diekmann & Kruppenbacher (1984). The advice given by such a system can ensure that the proper procedure for handling a claim is followed and can also make an evaluation of the likelihood of success with the claim. d'Agapeyeff & Hawkins (1987) describe a system to offer advice at the design stage of gas production systems about the corrosion life of the steel tubing. An interesting feature is its use of default values for certain operating parameters initially unknown. These values lead to conservative advice which is hardened up when the parameters are known. A task taking up to half a day of the expert's time has been taken off his shoulders, takes less time, and the design team can now try more alternatives. Reinschmidt & Finn (1986) describe a system which selects the most appropriate welding procedure according to the types of material being welded, the type of weld required, etc., and prints the procedure out ready for the welder. It is used on site.

Levitt & Kunz (1987) describe the PLATFORM series of expert systems which offer advice on construction planning. Rules are used to identify common sub-activities in completed activities which are either ahead of or behind schedule. These sub-activities are looked for in future activities whose time estimates are then modified accordingly. Rules to modify activity times according to when weather-sensitive activities occur in the year are also used to activate a dynamic Gantt chart display.

Finally, in this group of advisory systems, is one example of a popular application — an intelligent 'front end' to a complex conventional program. Finite element programs are now widely used for stress analysis, often by people who do not understand the theory and its limitations. Taig (1986) has developed an expert system to advise users of such programs. It is not concerned with the simple problem of data preparation, but tackles the real problem of how the engineering artefact to be stressed should be properly and accurately modelled by a set of finite elements. Advice is given about the types of element to be used, what sort of mesh should be drawn and what the costs will be. One feature is that the user is allowed to override this system at intermediate points and substitute his own idea for the system to use — an interesting notion of negotiation.

3.4 DATA INTERPRETATION SYSTEMS

Not far removed from advice based upon answers to questions is advice based upon analysis of some recorded data. In some instances, the problem is one of tackling huge quantities of data and drawing some conclusions; in others, the data may be modest in scale but may have to be extracted from some source before being analysed. As before, the only advice the expert system can offer is that which is predefined as its goal.

3.4.1 Interpretation of water penetrating a window frame
In places where tropical rain storms combine with high winds, there are severe problems in designing window frames to keep the rain out. Thomson (1986) describes an expert system which examines a cross-section of a window frame and considers all possible routes by which water might penetrate the frame. It is based upon the expertise of many years of testing commercial frames at CSIRO, Division of Building Research, Melbourne. The system has a facility to input and display the geometric details of a frame as a set of polygonal objects. The user, when defining these, specifies where they touch — potential paths for water to flow along. The system then determines from its knowledge base, which surfaces will have rain falling on them and shows this in the display as illustrated in Fig. 3.4. Rules are then used to

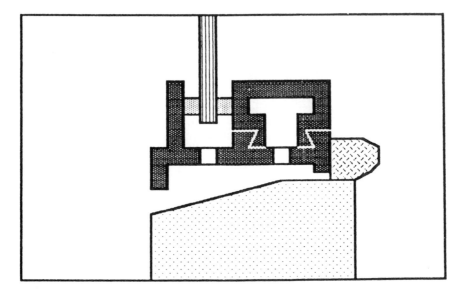

Fig. 3.4 — Window frame evaluated by WATERPEN.

discover how water can get from one place to another — by creeping, by surface tension, by wind effect and by dripping. The display shows how water passes through a frame and illustrates the passage graphically.

The system is written in PROLOG, and Thomson discusses many matters of general interest to expert system workers such as the advantages and disadvantages of PROLOG and the importance of graphics to users of expert systems.

3.4.2 Other interpretation systems
Reinschmidt & Finn (1986) report on a proposal to develop a system to process the large volumes of output we have come to expect from project management software.

To interpret such a pile and answer the single question 'Is the project running smoothly?' is the desirable target of this proposal. Maser (1986) describes research into a system to process large volumes of raw radar data of bridge decks along with data describing the bridge decks and their construction. The system uses knowledge which can conclude from the raw data whether the bridge deck is suffering from delamination caused by corrosion of the reinforcement. This is potentially a very important extension of remote sensing techniques. A smaller scale system for evaluating non-destructive tests on forgings is briefly outlined by Jacobs (1987). Completed systems for interpreting measurements of vibrations in rotating machines are reported by Reinschmidt & Finn (1986). In this example, vibration data are collected and analysed by standard monitoring equipment. The expert system asks questions about the results of that analysis and about the details of the machine, and then provides the user with a ranked list of probable causes of vibration out of 18 goals which may be taken singly or in combination.

Returning to the construction industry, a system for interpreting graphical data has been described by Bowén et al. (1986). This system examines a brick building to consider whether its design follows good practice. The interesting feature is that the source of data is an outline drawing of the walls drawn on the AUTOCAD CAD program. The expert system starts by analysing the drawing and extracting from it logical and numerical data from which it can draw conclusions by applying the knowledge built up in a set of rules.

Dym et al. (1988) describe a similar but more ambitious system which takes a floor plan of a building drawn with the Graph/Net CAD program and, after a pre-calculation phase to determine travel paths and their lengths, decides whether the design satisfies the Life Safety Code of the US National Fire Protection Authority. It is not clear whether the pre-calculation phase is entirely automatic since it depends upon the correct use of certain drawing techniques, but it is a very interesting use of expert system technology. Hosking et al. (1987) describe an expert system to do a similar task for the New Zealand fire safety code but with a conventional conversational interface.

3.5   MONITORING AND CONTROL SYSTEMS

Monitoring is the interpretation of data as they are collected. Its importance in the construction industry is perhaps greatest in the control of the processing of water and sewage. With the increased measurement of flows and depths, telemetered to central control desks, manual operators can easily be swamped with data. Expert systems to interpret the data and report only on the unusual are being developed. It is a short step to see the place of such systems in control. The digestion of sewage is an example of such a potential application. The large number of different types of bacteria involved and the varied mixes of materials to be broken down defy conventional analysis of the control of a sewage plant. But operators of such plants have experience which can be represented in a knowledge base. It is unlikely that the control loop would be automatic, but we can expect expert systems to be in the loop offering advice to the operators based upon continuous analysis of the measured data.

3.5.1   Monitoring a water supply, drainage, and sewerage network

Thomson *et al.* (1987) describe in a very thoughtful and comprehensive paper the development of a monitoring system for the Melbourne and Metropolitan Board of Works. Their Melbourne water and sewerage installation is a large, highly interconnected network of pipes, pumps, reservoirs, tanks, valves and treatment plants. There are over 200 sewerage pumping stations. The performance of the system is continuously monitored by telemetry, and 15 to 30 conditions are measured at each location. The staff monitoring the layout do not have detailed knowledge of each station in the network, and an expert system is being developed to help them reach an appropriate response when problems arise.

The expert system has two principal decisions to take — what is the most appropriate type of technician to send out to fix a fault, e.g. electrician, mechanic, etc., and when should the person be sent. The paper discusses very fully the challenges involved in creating a suitable knowledge base particularly for handling the problem of multiple alarms arising almost simultaneously. There is an excellent discussion of the effort made to ensure that the explanations the system offers are clear and concise. An interesting conclusion was that, contrary to the experts' predictions, there was no difficulty in applying the knowledge about one installation to a network of many installations. This illustrates the strength of the expert system approach.

3.5.2   Other monitoring systems

Palmer & Tull (1987) also describe a water management system which although not currently on-line could clearly be. It is concerned with providing guidance in managing water resources during a drought and is based upon records of past rainfalls and reservoir levels over nearly 50 years in the Seattle area.

The control of heating and ventilating systems in buildings has become so sophisticated that there are now not enough experts to ensure that they are correctly set up. Shaw (1986) describes an expert system which will assist in this work. BREXBAS takes as its input the monitored data of the performance of a building and produces a time-based continuous report on the status of the plant, identifying malfunctions as they occur.

3.6   DESIGN SYSTEMS

Automated design by a 'black box' may not be a desirable target, but perhaps there is a case for expert systems to turn out competent designs for simple parts of a building such as staircases or room layouts. Applying expert systems to design is very much at the research stage.

Rosenman *et al.* (1986) describe a system which can either check a room layout or create one to satisfy defined requirements; both use the same knowledge base. Tommelein *et al.* (1987) describe a system which designs the layout of temporary facilities on a construction site. Both papers illustrate the challenge of handling spatial arrangements within the context of design.

Part II

4

How a simple shell works —
an object oriented approach

This chapter acts as a bridge linking the introduction of Part I to the more detailed considerations of various topics in Part II. The presentation will be based upon the Simple Shell listed in Appendix 2 and available from the author. It will not be necessary to have the shell to understand this chapter, but, of course, having it will help. The shell has been designed to be a tutor by showing how it works as well as to show how an object oriented approach simplifies the creation of comprehensible rules. Instructions to use the program and some programming details of the shell, which is written in BASIC, are in Appendix 1.

4.1 CONNECTIONS BETWEEN OBJECTS AND RULES

A knowledge base, as we have seen, consists of rules which refer to objects. The main task of a shell is to draw inferences from the rules during a consultation by searching them and evaluating them as quickly as possible. This is made easier by establishing certain connections between the objects and rules, namely:

(a) which objects are used in each rule (in the antecedents)?
(b) which rules derive values for objects (as a consequent)?

It is also important to determine which objects will be evaluated by asking the user a question and which objects will be evaluated by processing one or more rules. Fig. 4.1 illustrates the connections and the types of objects in a few rules taken from the borehole example of Chapter 2.

How should a shell determine these connections, the type of each object, and the range of possible answers for the questions? There is a seductive simplicity in passing the whole of this task over to the shell and getting it to analyse the rules to find what object names are used, either in the antecedents or consequents, before a consultation starts. Many shells do this, and it provides a satisfyingly instant-prototyping way of constructing a knowledge base. It is enough to just type in two or three rules

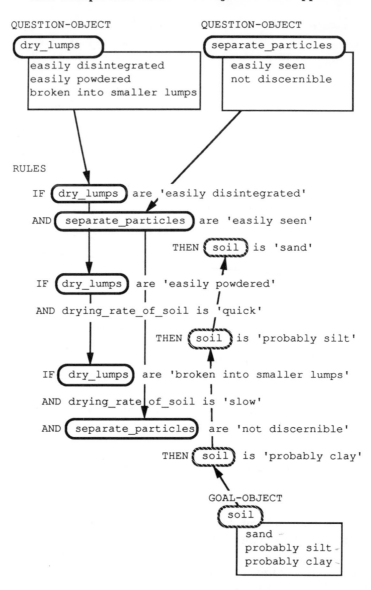

Fig. 4.1 — Connections between objects and rules.

and one has immediately an expert system which asks questions, concludes with an answer and does this with professional screen displays. When developing larger, more practical expert systems, however, some difficulties in this approach become apparent. A single mistake when typing an object name in a new rule generates a 'new' object — it may be detected by some shells because it appears once only in one rule, but not all shells are so skilful. Two objects for the same fact may be deliberately but inadvertently created simply because in a large knowledge base one had forgotten that the object had already appeared in earlier rules. It is also unsatisfactory to leave it to the shell to generate automatically some questions such as, 'What is the value of —', rather than to be able to specify precisely the text of a question to be put to the user.

This all leads to an alternative view of creating knowledge bases: that the important items to start with are not the rules but the objects. There is an interesting parallel here to conventional programming where the planning of appropriate data structures is now seen to be the key step to be completed before coding commences. For similar reasons, the discipline of thinking about objects before devising the rules leads to a more consistent knowledge base. Clearly the errors discussed above are less likely, but also the range of possible answers to each question will be made more coherent by being planned together. Other benefits derived from this approach are consistency checks on users' answers — a topic to be discussed in Chapter 5. Much of recent research in expert systems concerns the development of ideas about objects and 'frames' of information, which will be expanded upon in Chapter 7.

What is an object? Clearly it is similar to a variable in conventional programming, but there are some real differences. The key features of an object are:

(a) an object must indicate whether it has been evaluated or not;
(b) the object must have a process by which it can be evaluated — by asking the user a question, by processing one or more rules, by performing a calculation or by referring to a data base;
(c) the object may store several values to represent a fact.

A further important distinction, which is not easy to grasp, is that, whereas a conventional variable merely refers to a cell of memory which can be used over again, an object represents a fact, and a further instance of that fact is a new and quite separate example. Some shells allow objects to retain all examples of facts evaluated during one consultation.

4.2 REPRESENTING OBJECTS AND RULES IN A SHELL

When adopting an object oriented approach, the developer of a knowledge base is required to define the objects before creating any rules. The following factors must be considered as each object is defined.

(a) What type of object is it? — question or goal.
(b) What object name best indicates the fact being represented?
(c) What are the possible values that object can have as its result?
(d) How can comprehensible rules be made from (b) and (c)?
(e) What question can be put to the user so that the answers in (c) make sense?, or
(f) what rule(s) can be used to evaluate this object?

Item (e) is needed only for question objects; item (f) is needed for goal objects and can be found by the shell by a simple scan of the rules before execution. To illustrate these ideas immediately with a practical application, we take one object from the borehole system — the question object that represents the way a dry lump crumbles between the fingers. For this we need:

NAME	dry_lumps
TYPE	question
POSSIBLE VALUES 1	'easily disintegrated'
2	'easily powdered'
3	'broken into smaller lumps'
TEXT OF QUESTION	'How would you describe the way a dry lump of soil crumbled between the fingers?'

If this object is defined as object number 1, it can now be used to create the proposition

dry_lumps ARE 'easily powdered'

by the data

OBJECT NUMBER	1
OPERATOR	ARE
CONSTANT	2

In the Simple Shell, the operator is selected from a menu, hence the proposition is created with just three numbers and is firmly based on the definition of the object.

We can now consider what information the shell needs to store about objects in order to use them at the execution stage. The Simple Shell stores the following:

NAME
TYPE OF OBJECT — goal, sub-goal, question
STATUS — whether evaluated or not
RULES to use if object is goal or sub-goal
TEXT and list of possible answers if object is a question
RESULT

A minor distinction can be made between objects to be evaluated by presenting the user with a menu of possible answers and objects to be given a numerical value. The former simply requires a suitable screen display of the text of the question and the menu of possible answers. The numerical question needs the text, of course, but also upper and lower limits on the acceptable range of input values.

Representing the rules in the shell now becomes a simple matter of storing the cross-references to the list of objects and their possible answers. But the rules must also indicate what form each proposition takes, whether a proposition has already been evaluated and, if so, with what result, and also whether the whole rule has been evaluated and again with what result. Thus, for each rule the shell must store the following:

STATUS OF THE RULE — unknown, true or false
RESULT
CONSEQUENT OBJECT to which the result is to be given

For each proposition —
    NUMBER of an object
    OPERATOR, e.g. =, IS, IS NOT, etc.
    VALUE from the list of possible answers for the object
    STATUS OF THE PROPOSITION — unknown, true or false

The connections between rules and objects discussed in section 4.1 are thus embodied in the stored representation of objects and rules. With all the objects and rules numbered the numbers form easy cross-references, making the connections we need. Thus, each rule will refer to the objects it uses. Conversely, each object will refer to the rules in which it appears as a consequent.

In section 4.1 we discussed how the cross-connections could be established either by the shell analysing the rules to locate the appearance of all objects or by the creator of the knowledge base defining the objects first and building up the rules from them. Some shells adopt a middle position allowing both, but there is a clear trend towards a more object-oriented input of knowledge bases.

4.3   BACKWARD CHAINING SEARCH METHOD BY RECURSION —
    VARIATIONS

As already seen in Chapter 1, the backward chaining method has proved to be a popular and very efficient searching method for expert systems of the type we are concerned with. As a reminder, the method attempts to find a value for a goal object by searching for and evaluating all rules which have that object as a consequent. If necessary, the search will extend back through a hierarchy of rules if sub-goal objects are found and their values needed. The method may be most simply controlled by feeding to it a list of goal objects in some order, probably the most likely order of the result.

The overall flow of the Simple Shell is suprisingly simple and can be described by three interlocking flowcharts, the first of which is shown in Fig. 4.2. Readers may be surprised to see in this figure that only the negative result of 'no conclusion' is displayed when all objects have been used up. That is because a positive result when an object is successfully evaluated is better displayed within the routine doing that evaluation.

We can turn to that task now — the central task of an expert system — getting a value for a given object. This proves to be a most entertaining computing task for reasons to be made clear. Fig. 4.3 shows the flowchart for this task and, without giving a blow-by-blow commentary on it, some features will be highlighted. Note first the decision 'Does it already have a value?'. The searching and updating of the knowledge base may cause a value to be given to an object *before* it is actually needed, hence the question. The second decision in the flowchart separates the simple question-objects from the more interesting goal-objects. The former only require a suitable screen presentation.

The evaluation of a goal-object is the central task of the shell as it makes inferences from its knowledge. The first step is to find the rules which refer to the given object as a consequent. This uses the cross-connections described in section 4.2. Each rule is checked to see whether it already has a value of true or false — again

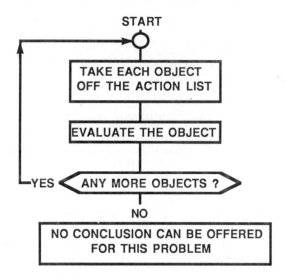

Fig. 4.2 — Overall flow of the Simple Shell.

the updating action could have caused this state to be found before the rule is used formally. If the rule has not been evaluated, the module of program to do that is entered (we shall look at that task next) but we do not assume success in that evaluation and look again at the status of the rule immediately afterwards. A successful evaluation leads, of course, to a result for the object; a failure leads on to trying all other rules for that object. If the object is a goal, then the result will be displayed and this is when the system comes to a successful conclusion and stops.

Lastly, we look at the task of evaluating a rule. The flowchart is in Fig. 4.4 and refers to rules which have propositions joined only by AND. (The use of OR and brackets adds an unnecessary complication for our purpose.) Because of this simplification, all propositions in the rule must be true for the rule to be true. If any one proposition is false, we need not evaluate the remaining propositions; the rule is false. In evaluating a proposition, the shell will consider the components of that proposition; for example, the first proposition of the first rule of the borehole example in Fig. 4.1 is:

> dry_lumps are 'easily disintegrated'

To evaluate this proposition, the shell needs the value of the object dry_lumps and here is the very interesting twist hinted at before. In the middle of the task of evaluating a rule, which is needed in the evaluation of an object, we need to evaluate another object! A case of

> 'Great fleas have little fleas upon their backs to bite 'em, and little fleas have lesser fleas and so ad infinitum'

> (Augustus de Morgan)

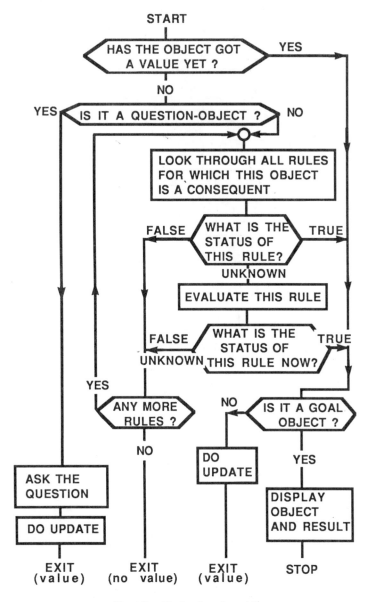

Fig. 4.3 — Evaluation of an object.

In programming terms, this process of a module of program calling itself is known as recursion. It allows the simple evaluation of objects within antecedents of one rule being themselves the consequent of another rule — indeed, the backward chaining method is seen as recursion proceeding to whatever depth of rule is needed. Some programming languages provide recursion automatically — the language BASIC in which the Simple Shell is written does not. Appendix 1 outlines the method whereby recursion is achieved.

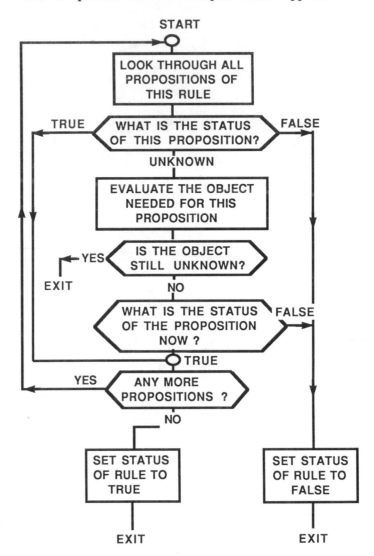

Fig. 4.4 — Evaluation of a rule.

It is appropriate at this point to illustrate the common and useful notion of considering a hierarchy of connected rules as a 'tree'. Fig. 4.5 shows a theoretical set of such rules as a tree: the objects are represented by the circles and the radiating lines represent the propositions of the rules. The tree is on its side with the goal object (the base of the tree) on the left and the question objects (the leaves of the tree) on the right. Evaluating the goal object involves working through layers of rules towards the question objects, and at any stage there is a route through the tree (shown by the heavy line) which represents the set of rules involved in the recursion. A tree is a useful subset of the whole network of connections in a knowledge base and

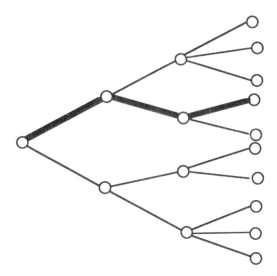

Fig. 4.5 — A 'tree' of rules.

reduces the scale of knowledge which must be considered at any time. The knowledge diagram in Fig. 3.1 is a practical example.

The Simple Shell adopts recursion in its backward chaining search, but this is not the only or indeed the obviously 'best' searching strategy to use for an efficient expert system. Consider the strategy implied by the method adopted. Starting with a goal-object to be evaluated, the shell tries the relevant rules in the order in which they appear in the knowledge base. Is that the best 'order' to get the result as quickly as possible during the 'average' consultation? Next, the recursion method adopted will automatically plunge down through all layers of rules upon rules without regard to what is 'best' in terms of computing effort. For example, it might be that the first proposition in a rule uses a sub-goal which requires several levels of rule to evaluate it, whereas the second proposition might depend only upon a question-object. In terms of computing effort, the cost of evaluating the first object will far exceed that for the second and, if the latter proves to be false, all the effort expended on evaluating the first would have been wasted. If we raise the question of what is the most effective object to evaluate at each stage of the consultation so as to have the greatest impact on the whole knowledge base or, at least, on the set of linked rules currently being examined, we open up a whole new set of searching strategies. Nilsson (1980) discusses many of these methods and Naylor (1984) presents some dynamic searching methods very simply. There are no simple answers to 'What is the best method?' and commercial shells do not all use the same method.

4.4 OPPORTUNISTIC FORWARD CHAINING — WHEN TO DO IT — DEMONS

In the dialogue between user and expert system, when a question is put and answered, the shell must use the information gained to its fullest. This is achieved by updating the whole knowledge base, not only for the value given to the question object, but for all the consequences that follow from the use of that object in any rule. The simplest consequence is that some propositions using the object are found to be false, leading to some rules being found false also. A more profound consequence could be that a proposition is made true and, if all other propositions in a given rule are already true, the whole rule becomes true. That this can happen whilst the shell is actually evaluating another rule brings out the dilemma of when to update.

But first the method. The Simple Shell adopts a simple strategy appropriate to small knowledge bases. All rules are examined and, if unknown, are evaluated by the same routine as used for the backward chaining stage but with one difference. If an unknown object is encountered, the rule is simply abandoned — recursion is not used. Instead, a note is made if *any* rule is successfully proved true during this sweep through the knowledge base. This will lead to a value being given to a new object. In that case, the whole updating process is repeated to take on board the effect of the new object now having a value, the process stopping only when no further rules are proved true.

There is probably less argument over this strategy than there is for backward chaining, but the simple search through all the rules described here can obviously be improved upon by linking objects to just those rules which *use* that object. More contentious is the question of when to update the knowledge base. This hinges upon whether a shell allows the use of a form of rule charmingly called demons which were slyly introduced in the borehole example of Chapter 2. Demons are rules which have as their consequent an action which is to be performed *immediately* the rule is proved to be true. The simplest action is a display on the computer screen of a message for the user. This could be advice, or a warning based upon answers already given. Another simple action is to force a question to be asked immediately. The Simple Shell provides both by the consequents:

*DISPLAY message
*ASK object name

These were used in the first two rules of the borehole knowledge base as follows:

IF organic_content is 'substantial'
THEN *DISPLAY 'Please answer the following questions by examining the non-organic part of your sample'

IF separate_particles are 'easily seen'
THEN *ASK particle_size_mm.

Clearly, both rules must be activated immediately the relevant object has the appropriate value. Hence, the inclusion of such demons demands that a shell must update its knowledge base whenever an object is given a value. Not all shells provide demons and, in that case, the updating can be delayed until the current rule has been finished with, i.e. proved to be true or false. In practice, the presence of demons with immediate updating provides a more 'natural' modelling of our reasoning processes since we expect any conclusion to be drawn and acted upon immediately the necessary facts are known.

4.5   CONTROL OF THE SEARCHING PROCESS

Apart from rules and objects, an expert system also needs some guidance about the preliminary questions to be asked and the order of the goals to be evaluated. Control is a badly thought out element of many shells, and some comments on the methods adopted and the importance of control will be made in later chapters. The Simple Shell uses a list, the ACTION list, of objects which are to be processed in order. These may be question objects or goal objects in any mixture, but usually the first few will be those objects that cause the chosen preliminary questions to be asked. Some writers refer to the control list as an 'agenda'.

This simple device provides a procedural control of the inferencing process which is quite independent of the order of the rules in the knowledge base. Not all shells have this, and the order of the rules does have an influence on the sequence of objects investigated. Other shells provide quite sophisticated means of control, allowing the sequence of goals to be juggled according to the user's answers to the early questions. A simple method is to introduce a demon of the form

> IF antecedents
> THEN *INVESTIGATE object name

When this rule is proved true, the object in the consequent is pushed into first place in the order of goals to be investigated. Intelligent use of this demon can quite radically improve the user friendliness of a system by making it concentrate on the goals considered most likely from the answers to the preliminary questions. The Simple Shell does not have this demon, but introducing it is one of several projects set out at the end of this chapter.

4.6   WHY AND HOW

The basis of explaining to the user 'Why' a question is being asked or 'How' a result was obtained must be the rules. The alternative of potted texts to substitute for this is dangerous owing to the real risk of rules and text getting out of step during development. However, it is not easy to present these explanations in anything other than a very wooden style, and some research is being applied to developing more acceptable presentations. Most shells simply dress up the rules, and the Simple Shell does no more.

Answering the question 'Why' is handled by displaying the name of the current object being evaluated and the rule being used to do that. When recursion is being used to step down through various levels of rules, the explanation is presented step-by-step starting from the current rule and then through the list of subordinate rules.

Answering the question 'How' a result was arrived at is more difficult since there may have been a wide 'tree' of rules involved in proving the result. Rather than show the whole set, it is perhaps better, and certainly easier, to show one rule at a time and to invite the user to select further objects and to see the rules which led to those values. The Simple Shell adopts this method.

4.7   SOME EXERCISES USING THE SIMPLE SHELL

Before tackling these exercises please read the instructions in Appendix 1.
(1)   Run the borehole example several times. Print out objects and rules and challenge yourself to predict the next question before the shell asks it.
(2)   Try the 'commentary' facility and check the status of rules and objects.
(3)   Create a new action list with objects in a new order and repeat (1).
(4)   Add some more demons to detect combinations of answers not covered, e.g.

> separate_particles are 'easily seen'
> AND dry_lumps are 'broken into small lumps'

which might indicate a mixture of sand and clay and be shown by a screen display.
(5)   Add some new rules — you do not have to be an expert geotechnician. For example, add some new goals of sandy_clay and sandy_silt, both containing 35-65% sand.
(6)   Develop your own knowledge base for a problem of diagnosis.

Programming projects for students
(1)   Add demons with *INVESTIGATE (section 4.5).
(2)   Develop the Simple Shell to allow rules to use the connective OR and brackets.
(3)   Develop the Simple Shell to include other searching strategies.
(4)   Develop the Simple Shell to allow multiple consequents to a rule.

5

Likely form of a diagnosis or advice system

There are dangers in attempting to make expert systems mimic too closely the behaviour of human experts in trying to give them a 'human face'. Diaper (1986) and others warn of the readiness with which users overestimate an expert system's knowledge and abilities. The famous mock-psychiatrist program ELIZA showed how readily people would hold intimate conversations with a system which had no intelligence but just a natural language interface. In suggesting, as in section 1.5, that the overall form of an expert system can profitably follow the stages a human expert takes, the author is not starting down the road to a construction industry android complete with voice recognition, voice generation and flashing green eyes! The virtues of considering the methods of a human expert lie in creating user-friendliness through a familiar, tolerant and comprehensible set of actions even though these are only messages and questions displayed on a screen.

Consider a visit to the most friendly, thoughtful, considerate expert (perhaps the old family doctor). What would be the pattern of the consultation? — certainly not an abrupt fusillade of bald questions in a confusing order leading to a curt diagnosis — as our current view of expert systems might lead to. No, it is likely that the consultation would fall into certain stages, perhaps with blurred edges.

(a) The expert would start with some general preliminary questions — and we would be disturbed if he did not. He would help us to answer the difficult ones and we would not be surprised if he raised an eyebrow at an answer and probed away to confirm it or to show us some inconsistency in our replies.

(b) He would move on to more detailed questions pertinent to the most likely causes of our problem as inferred from our answers to the preliminary questions. We would not be surprised if he was quite persistent in his questions at this stage (but see (d) below).

(c) He would report his findings to us in a simple fashion. We would not expect a regurgitation of all the paths he took mentally during the consultation, but only a description in terms we could understand of the final conclusion.

(d) He would keep us informed of his progress and thoughts, particularly if the investigation became extended and time-consuming and, especially, if it had to be suspended for some tests to be made.

Being aware of (and reacting to) these stages as an expert system is developed leads to a more acceptable product. Each stage deserves separate consideration and needs distinct software facilities to achieve a mature result.

5.1 PRELIMINARY QUESTIONS — ASKING, HELPING, CHECKING

There are at least four aspects to this stage:

(a) What questions should be included in this set?
(b) How can we ensure they are asked in an appropriate order?
(c) What help, if it is needed, can the user be given to answer the question?
(d) How can the answers be checked for consistency?

If a record of the consultation is to be kept, perhaps automatically on a disc file, a few identification questions will be needed first; these are best kept to a minimum. In deciding upon the rest of the preliminary questions, the key is to look for those which occur most frequently in the rules of the knowledge base. Thus, when analysing the borehole knowledge, we noted that particle size was a commonly needed fact in many rules and was therefore made a preliminary question. In the dampness system described in section 3.1, preliminary questions which determined the size, age and type of building were followed by more questions which located and classified the dampness. These formed a natural set of ten preliminary questions and were selected before knowledge elicitation commenced in anticipation of their importance in the rules. Fig. 5.1 shows the full set of these questions.

Ensuring that these questions are asked in order requires a facility in the chosen shell to exert some control over its searching process. There is a variety of control methods implemented in shells and most are inadequate. It is not simply that the preliminary questions must be asked in a given order, but that all stages of the consultation need controlling. For the purposes of the preliminary questions, the simplest control method is a list of objects in the order in which they are to be evaluated. The Simple Shell adopts this. An improvement on this method is to positively prevent the main diagnosis starting until all preliminary questions have been asked, but not to disable any rules included to check consistency in the answers to the questions. The argument for this more sophisticated level of control is that users can be disconcerted by conclusions being displayed about the final diagnoses whilst they are still answering the preliminary questions — better to let them finish those first.

Providing help to a user faced with a difficult question requires another software facility but one which is usually available in most shells. The creator of the knowledge base types in an appropriate 'help' text, and the user can have this displayed on the screen if desired before answering the question, often by simply pressing a function key. What is often overlooked is the considerable knowledge that can be embodied in this type of text. Cooper (1987) draws attention to this in a system to help a planning engineer select the right type of crane for a multi-storey construction project. A key calculation in this is of how many hours of lifting are needed, and this

What is the main usage of the building?

How old is the building?

How many storeys has the building got?

What is the roof covering?

What is the angle of pitch?

In which storey does the dampness occur?

Where in the room does the dampness occur?

What form does the dampness take?

What is the shape of the stain?

How is the dampness distributed round the room?

**How many patches of dampness
are there in the room?**

Fig. 5.1 — Preliminary questions of BREDAMP.

depends upon the rate of lifting for many different items of material and plant. These rates represent an important part of the total knowledge of the system and are presented to the user as 'help' texts. Other systems use this 'help' facility to explain jargon, to amplify the question text with a diagram and even to give a short tutorial.

Checking the consistency of the user's answers is perhaps the most overlooked aspect of a human expert's way of working. Trethowan (1987) in a thoughtful discussion on uncertainty starts, 'Humans generally, including experts, are quite accustomed to receiving information ranging from accurate to misleading to totally false and sifting this subconsciously to extract the true and useful.' Expert systems must at least attempt a similar filtering. We can indentify three conclusions from rules for checking a user's answer — accept, reject, advise against but will accept. Not all answers can be checked but, to determine what checks are possible and how they are to be made, one should at least consider 'good practice' and any physical relationships between objects. For example, in the dampness system already alluded to, a damp stain on an internal wall and next to a window is most unlikely. In the paint system described in section 3.2, a user choosing to have the finish coat put on in the workshop before erection would be warned of the likelihood of having this finish scratched during erection and asked again where the finish is to be applied. If he insists on using the workshop, the answer is accepted.

The software facility needed for checking is the provision of modularity in the rule base — and few shells provide this. Modularity means 'parcelling up' rules into sub-sets associated with single tasks — we are used to having this facility as subroutines or procedures of programming languages. The same need exists in expert systems, and checking users' answers is one example of the need. There is no point in cluttering up a main rule set concerned with the meat of a diagnosis problem with those rules simply concerned with checking an answer to a question. In section 7.4 we illustrate how the modular feature of one shell can be used for this task with the benefit of reducing the size of the main rule base.

'Demons' provide an ideal facility for issuing warnings to users because they are acted upon immediately they are found to be true. Demons can be devised to warn of bad practice such as in the paint example above, to warn of conflicts in answers or to reject impossible answers — all the actions a human expert takes as we answer his questions.

The whole topic of improving 'user interfaces' is a very active area of current research. The most notable thrusts attempt to recognize that users will have different background knowledge and that therefore expert systems must be made more flexible in their questioning. Methods to handle this include allowing the user to volunteer data even to the point of nominating which goals are to be first investigated, devising an expert system so that it nominates and investigates the most likely goals after asking a bare minimum of questions and of developing an adaptive interface which recognizes the level of expertise of the user and reacts by asking more or less questions. Berry & Broadbent (1987) survey recent work in this area.

5.2 STRATEGY — ORDERING THE SEQUENCE OF GOALS — IMPORTANCE OF CONTROL

The answer to the preliminary questions may eliminate some goals immediately and will probably suggest an order in which the remainder can be investigated. The overriding need here is for sophisticated control, but one aspect of strategy can be dealt with first. A decision should be taken as to whether the system will stop when a goal is found to be true, or whether it should continue through all goals and report on any found true. Diagnosis systems, in particular, may have such uncertainty in the knowledge base as to suggest that a safe strategy is to examine all possible causes and accept that, by selecting several, the expert system has at least made a contribution to solving the problem by narrowing the field. In this case, there is little point in re-ordering the goals as a result of the answers to the preliminary questions. Where diagnosis is more confident and the system is to stop when a goal is proved true, it becomes important and even essential to rearrange the goals at run time. In a telecommunications fault-detection system the author developed, certain faults had to be examined first to clear the way for a second set to be considered. The order in which the sets were examined changed over according to the answers to the preliminary questions. Fig. 5.2 illustrates the overall flow of such a system, and this needs a more dynamic control system than the simple investigation list of goals suitable for ordering the preliminary questions. 'Demons' that add goals to an investigation list, as described in Chapter 4, provide a clumsy means of control. Ideally, what is needed is a top level procedural language with all the facilities of a conventional programming language below which the backward and forward chain-

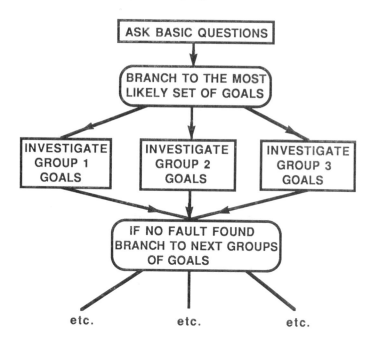

Fig. 5.2 — Part of the flow of a telecommunications system.

ing search busies itself making inferences, perhaps on self-contained modules of knowledge. A few shells provide facilities of this nature.

5.3 REPORTING AND KEEPING THE USER INFORMED

What sort and form of report is needed at the end of a consultation will vary according to the purpose of an expert system. If it is designed to offer advice to a professional who will then incorporate that advice in further work, a formal printed report may not be needed. On the other hand, if the system is designed for widespread use by untrained people, a self-contained printed report may be mandatory. It might include date and time, a summary of the answers to the preliminary questions and the conclusion, so as to form a complete record of the consultation. It may go further and include the recommended actions to take. Some, but not all, shells recognize this need and provide a specific 'reporting' facility. The most flexible of these allow many separate contributions to be made to the report, each indicating where it is to appear in the final version.

Keeping the user informed by answering the questions, 'Why is this question being asked?' and 'How was this result obtained?', are central features of expert systems already discussed (sections 1.4 and 4.6) and are provided to varying standards by most shells. Answering the question, 'Why was this result not obtained?', is not usually provided but can be very helpful to a user. The dampness system, section 3.1, has extra rules (demons) to force a display to appear when each goal is disproved. These rules are additional to the diagnosis rules and cannot just be the consequents of the antecedents becoming false. There may be several rules in the knowledge base, each referring to the same consequent goal — as in the masonry example of Fig. 1.3 where three rules all lead to the same cause. A rule to explain why that cause was not selected must be an additional rule.

Not all users will want to see these dismissals at every consultation, and this can be handled by asking, perhaps as the first of the preliminary questions, if the 'Why not' displays are to be shown. The answer to this question must also be embodied in the demons which control these displays. A quite different solution to this problem was adopted for the paint selection system. The LEONARDO shell used allowed conclusions about each paint, i.e. 'suitable' or 'unsuitable', to be displayed with the user given the option of selecting any such conclusion and seeing the rules which led to that result — this handled nicely both 'Why?' and 'Why not?'.

5.4 OTHER MISCELLANEOUS SOFTWARE FACILITIES

It is appropriate here to list the standard facilities one expects of a professional computer program and which complete the description of the overall form of an expert system. It is very useful to be able to keep a record of a consultation on a disc file — this is often called a 'log'. These are particularly useful for post mortems on evaluation tests or when resolving a doubt about a conclusion. Also useful, is a facility to suspend a consultation part way through, saving the current state of the system on a disc file and allowing a re-start at that point at a later time. Apart from allowing for interruptions in normal usage, this is a useful feature when testing alternative answers to later questions after a fixed initial sequence of answers.

6

Knowledge acquisition

In general, knowledge is obtainable from books, from examples, and from people. If knowledge can be satisfactorily represented on paper, it may well be not an appropriate topic for an expert system. The step-by-step procedural nature of many codes of practice is one example mentioned earlier. But books and reports are our most common form of knowledge and many will, at least, provide a starting point for the knowledge acquisition task. Extracting knowledge from many examples is a possibility which has attracted artificial intelligence researchers and will be discussed briefly later. The principal sources of knowledge with which we will be concerned are human experts and so we consider the task of 'eliciting' their knowledge. Much has been written of the difficulty of this task, and it certainly is not easy. However, other professionals such as social scientists and management consultants have been at it for years, and at least some of the pitfalls are known. Berry & Broadbent (1986) briefly survey current methods and do not find that knowledge acquisition is a major bottleneck in the production of expert systems. This is obviously not a 'hard' science and there are no fixed solutions. This chapter outlines some commonly held ideas of how to go about it, laced with some experience gained in practice.

6.1 BASIC PROBLEMS IN KNOWLEDGE ELICITATION

As stated already in section 2.2, the underlying problem in knowledge elicitation is one of communication between one or more experts and one or more interviewers. We shall look at both parties shortly, but it is best to keep in mind certain basic ideas.

(a) The objective is to convert the expert's knowledge to the form used by a shell program.
(b) Analysis of the knowledge to accomplish this conversion will go on in parallel with the knowledge elicitation.
(c) Experts 'apparently' solve problems by working through a set of sequential steps. We need to get at the reasoning that lies behind these steps.
(d) Knowledge elicitation and the creation of an expert system is an iterative process.

It may not be necessary for the interviewer to know how to code the chosen shell, but it is certainly important that he understands the principles of rules and inferencing. If he does not prepare the final knowledge base, another communications gap with the programmer must be bridged. (One method is the 'paper model', section 6.5.) Achieving objective (a) will be easier if the interviewer does the coding too, as will the ongoing analysis of the overall form of the system. It is very helpful to establish at an early stage the general flow, maybe as set out in Chapter 5, and to start identifying intermediate stages, i.e. sub-goals. These should be discussed with the expert. Our experience is that most experts quickly understand the idea of rules and will want to be involved in their formulation and the decisions on the overall form. This is, in any case, all part of achieving that desirable end result of the expert being entirely able to understand the final knowledge base.

Item (c) represents a paradox which will probably always bedevil knowledge elicitation. Experts are good at solving problems — that is why we go to them — and they do this (apparently) by following a procedural sequence of questions and deductions. We can watch them do this on real problems or look through case studies with them retrospectively. If we were able to capture their knowledge in conventional programs, this forward-chaining procedural-sequence would be fine and life would be easy. But it is just because an expert's knowledge cannot easily be represented by conventional programs that we use expert system technology and are forced to look behind the external manifestation of the expert's thinking and made to capture the true basis of the reasoning behind it. Of course, rules and backward-chaining are a poor simulation of human reasoning, but it is all we have and we must try to represent the expert's thinking by these means. And so the paradox is to take the 'case study' procedural appearance of an expert's way of working and turn it into rules which, when searched, will lead to a similar, if not identical, set of questions and deductions. Most experts think they are quite good at helping in this conversion — and some are quite good too! To be aware of this paradox and to be aware of the nature of this task is at least to be forewarned.

The task of knowledge elicitation and the build-up of a knowledge base is an iterative process, and the experts and interviewers must be quite aware of this from the start. It is one of the attractions of expert systems that early prototypes can be put together quickly. Some comments on the advantages and disadvantages of this will be made later — it certainly does help in this iterative refinement to be able to show the expert the developing system. All parties should be aware, however, that adding to and editing the knowledge base may be a permanent task. This should not be a surprise — codes of practice are continually being revised to keep them up to date.

6.2   THE EXPERTS AND THE INTERVIEWERS

Choosing your expert and motivating him are keys to the production of a successful expert system. Of course, you may not be able to choose — if there were lots of experts in a topic, there would probably be no need for an expert system. But, if there is only one, do not assume that he is necessarily omniscient. A little reading by the interviewer may, in any case, help to understand the topic but might also ensure that the expert is kept on his toes. Having several experts leads to group problems to be discussed shortly.

Whether it is one or many, motivating the expert to be truly enthusiastic about the expert system is very, very important. The ideal situation comes when the expert himself has proposed the development of the system to relieve him of the simpler, tedious cases so allowing him time to enjoy the more interesting problems. Be suspicious of the expert who volunteers a little time to help out a non-expert academic enthusiastic about this new technology. More difficult to assess is the motivation of the expert who has been directed to help create a system by higher management. There are no limits to the threats a human may perceive in such a directive — is it redundancy, is it sideways promotion once all expertise is imparted, is it a devious ploy of management to reduce staff numbers? An expert may be reluctant simply from the fear of being exposed as a non-expert. Knowledge elicitation is certainly going to be an uphill struggle if motivation is not certain, and some quiet confirmation may be needed of the enthusiasm of the expert and the management.

Handling a group of experts does raise some other problems, although it obviously confers some advantages by bringing more minds to the task with all the benefits which accrue from the resulting sparks. Conflicts over rules will arise and must be resolved by human means — many people seem to expect the expert system to do it! It may be that a conflict indicates ignorance, and resolution will need study/research of that area. It may only need compromise which may be more easily seen by the interviewer. A more difficult problem, because it does not surface as vividly as a knowledge conflict, is the interaction between the experts. One report of a panel of experts suggested that, 'the discussions emphasized complexities of theory and concealed simplicities of practice'. Two prima donnas in a group of experts can easily drag discussion off to esoteric corners whilst simultaneously swamping the quieter experts. We have found that panel meetings should be balanced by individual interviews of all the experts. One might add too, that multiple interviewers can create problems — one expert faced by such a battery complained of an 'inquisition'.

From experience, two warnings can be sounded about experts' expectations of expert systems. Some non-computer people expect computers to be able to reason about geometric problems and spatial relationships with the same ease as humans. Regrettably, they cannot do so yet — it is a topic of current AI research. A two-year-old child can instantly say whether a given point lies inside or outside an irregular shape; a computer has to do much work to draw that conclusion. Extending that problem to 3-D geometric questions such as, 'Will the jib of a crane hit the sloping roof of this building?', requires much computational effort and should be avoided in present day expert systems. Similarly, the embodiment of fundamental causal knowledge such as the force of gravity, Newton's laws of motion, etc., is beyond current expert system technology. Experts must represent the effect of these scientific fundamentals in rules for each particular situation. Interviewers — the jargon phrase of 'knowledge engineer' is too pretentious to use and there is, in any case, no element of *engineering* in the task — should, of course, be aware of the basic ideas set out above and particularly the paradox of converting procedures to rules. That is not the only challenge they face. The tasks of an interviewer are to prompt the expert, to note the responses, to comprehend the ideas, to remember and recall earlier references to facts and to analyse the whole. It is a formidable task, and we shall look at methods in section 6.4. Whatever method is used, the interviewer must guard against assuming knowledge himself. Some writers argue that the ideal interviewer has no knowledge initially of the topic. That seems an extreme position and will cause the expert to spend time on basics and puts on the interviewer the onus of learning these fast. The author believes that a relevant background knowledge is very helpful, but the interviewer must be humble and carefully inquisitive when meeting the expert.

The need for care can be illustrated by a simple rule for a trivial problem. Imagine an expert system which simply decides from the lengths of the three sides whether a triangle is equilateral, isosceles or general. The rule for an isosceles triangle might be:

> IF $a=b$
> OR $b=c$
> OR $c=a$
> THEN triangle is isosceles

Is that a correct rule? Will it handle all cases? The answer is no, since the rule would be proved true if all sides were equal and the triangle was equilateral. The correct rule is:

> IF $(a=b$ AND $b<>c)$
> OR $(b=c$ AND $c<>a)$
> OR $(c=a$ AND $a<>b)$
> THEN triangle is isosceles

Knowledge elicitation does need that sort of careful, formal, very precise way of working. It is a hint to the type of interviewer needed too — perhaps there is after all a place in this world for the quiet, deep-thinking tortoise rather than the noisy, extrovert hare.

Finally, it should be recorded that at least one expert found the experience of having his knowledge elicited was rewarding and invigorating — other writers have noted the same effect. The discipline of setting down his knowledge in a goal-oriented manner brought a new perspective to his own thinking about his specialism. In turn this caused a change in the presentation of his expertise when talking to others.

6.3   DEFINING THE SCOPE OF THE EXPERT SYSTEM — INVOLVING THE INTENDED USERS

As for any project, time must be spent in defining the problem to be tackled. If it is a first expert system, caution will in any case suggest starting with a quite modest diagnosis problem. Even if it is not the first, some questions need to be asked:

(a) Is it a diagnosis or a selection system?
(b) Is a motivated expert available with time to spare?
(c) Who will use it and where?
(d) How should the expert system record its advice?
(e) What are the expectations of management?
(f) How big will the system be and how long will it take to develop?

Previous chapters and sections have discussed (a) and (b). Answering (c) and (d) provides an opportunity to involve the intended users who are so often overlooked. Diaper (1988), in a thorough consideration of who will be affected by an expert system, identifies direct users and indirect users, the latter being those influenced by its introduction without actually using it. It is not easy to involve users at an early stage since, until a decent prototype has been created, the intended users cannot see what they are supposed to comment on. (One of the dangers of using early prototypes for this is the 'turn off' risked by showing a version with trivial knowledge.) At least the developers should be asked to consider questions (c) and (d) before starting work. Their answers will indicate the level to which questions should go, whether technical jargon will be acceptable or not, what sort of 'help' text should be included, and whether the final advice should be displayed on the screen or printed out in a form to be filed. As for (e), it is always as well to know what management expects from a computer project — it may be advisable to keep their hopes as modest as possible when first engaged in this technology.

Predicting the answers to question (f) for conventional programs has baffled computer managers for years. Expert systems have some features which at least act as parameters. A measure of and a constraint on the size of an expert system is the number of goals it will have. Since these are the faults or causes to be diagnosed or the pieces of advice to be offered, it makes good sense and is good practice to agree on them at the very beginning. Indeed, the first knowledge elicitation sessions should be directed to drawing them out and defining them precisely, and this work might be done before even agreeing to embark on the development of the system. It is a task which may be easier when tackled with a group of experts and near-experts, i.e. managers who used to be experts. Further, having agreed upon a list of goals, they can serve as a definition of the system with proposals for further goals being forbidden or assigned to future development.

Converting that parameter to an estimate of system size and time to develop, is, of course, hazardous. Obviously, the number of rules will reflect the difficulty of the topic, and we have considered using the time an expert typically takes in a consultation as a measure of that difficulty. For the systems the author has been involved in, this is measured in hours rather than days, e.g. half an hour to a few hours of the expert's time to solve a problem. The ratio of rules to goals for these systems has been between five and ten. This figure is for shells which allow rules to join propositions by OR as well as AND. Shells which do not, need many more rules. Estimating the time needed to develop the system of course depends on the lucidity of the expert and the experience of the interviewer in analysing and representing the knowledge for a chosen shell. Some indications were given in Chapter 3 for two of the systems completed by the author.

6.4 A METHOD OF KNOWLEDGE ELICITATION

It is becoming clear that the basic method is a mixture of the following:
  (a) Unstructured general interviews.
  (b) Interviews focused on one goal or topic.

(c) Use of past problems.
(d) Demonstration and discussion of prototype.
(e) Discussion of knowledge base with expert.

Other methods not experienced by the author are:

(f) Watching and questioning an expert at work.
(g) Playing role of expert and being criticized by him.
(h) Giving expert deliberately vague specification of a problem.
(j) Getting experts to rank symptoms in priority order when linked to a goal.

We shall discuss ideas (a) to (e).

The unstructured interview should be aimed at educating the interviewer and establishing the scope of the system by defining the list of goals. The expert should be allowed to do this in his manner, even if it seems rambling to the interviewer — this is definitely the time for the interviewer to be a sponge soaking up the jargon, the task, and the ideas involved. Clearly, some direction may be appropriate, particularly to get that all important list of goals drawn up. This is the time when a good relationship can be built up between interviewer and expert, a 'chemistry' which will pay dividends when ground needs to be retraced or delicate questions to be put about the standing of a rule. The focused interviews can merge into the first general interviews, but it may be best to make clear to the expert that the transition has occurred. Ideally, the interviewer should now concentrate discussion on one goal at a time and be concerned about the symptoms and rules which confirm that goal alone. Some experts find this easy, some — probably most — not. Experts who have tried to train others are more likely to have thought out how they work and how their knowledge can be communicated. Even so, getting them to think in terms of rules will not be easy, particularly if there are many intermediate stages between the symptoms and the goal. As an illustration from the dampness system described in Chapter 3, the knowledge about 'dampness due to a leaking pipe' was broken down into the following stages:

Goal	Pipe leakage
First level	Pipe above a ceiling, in a floor, in a wall
Second level	Supply pipe or drainage pipe
Third level	Condensation on pipe instead of leakage
	Result of tests on a drainage pipe

The knowledge diagram in Fig. 3.1 shows the links between these levels in more detail. It will be apparent that breaking down the knowledge in this way concentrates attention on smaller and smaller details which proves helpful in the knowledge elicitation work. Experts who can work this way may be distracted from the current goal by the possibility that a symptom could also be an indicator for another goal — their normal procedural working method breaking through. It is one advantage of the backward-chaining method of searching rules to be able to say there, 'Yes, we will note that for the future but today we are concentrating on this goal'. For these ideal experts, case studies can be used for tests of the symptom. Verification is a topic of Chapter 8 but, clearly, trials of the system against the expert form a part of that.

Case study material is ideal for these tests but should be used also in the first instance to help develop the knowledge.

Experts who cannot work backwards from a goal to the symptoms are more difficult to work with. It becomes necessary to note every question they ask and every decision they take and to back-track over these to determine the significance, if any, of alternative answers. Case studies provide ideal material to 'talk through' such analyses. If case studies are not available, it may be necessary to adopt method (f) and to watch the expert at his job. In either case, the interviewer has to take a more active role in creating the knowledge base. It can be done but will take longer.

No matter what type of expert you have, this is the stage where real knowledge will be discussed. It hardly needs saying to trained professionals that at this detailed stage, rules should be devised to represent true causal relationships between facts and a consequence based upon scientific principles. Rules of thumb should be avoided if at all possible. It may be that a relationship is not fully understood but has some basis and has been observed many times — that would be acceptable. A crescent-shaped stain in the top corner of two walls and a ceiling is a good indicator of condensation if humidity is present. Proving this shape by thermodynamics would be quite a challenge, but the basic mechanics can be seen and the phenomenon has been observed enough times to accept that there is a causal relationship. On the other hand, a rule that 'activities will overshoot if there is an R in the month' would be a poor sort of relationship for the effect of weather in a project management system.

Two suggestions may be made to assist this detailed work. Quite often, an expert will base decisions on a fact which is measured by a graded response from a low to a high value. The severity of exposure to corrosive conditions for example could vary from 'low' to 'very severe'. Care needs to be taken at the knowledge elicitation stage to ensure that such facts are represented in a way which is suitable both to the user when answering the question and to the expert when looking at the rules. In section 7.2 we discuss the advantages and disadvantages of using a numerical scale for such responses. It is not a simple matter to find an alternative, and this problem should be considered early in the knowledge elicitation. The second suggestion concerns identifying questions which are mandatory and those which are not. Some shells allow the user to answer 'don't know' to a question. Knowing whether this is allowed by the intended shell will influence the knowledge elicitation since it affords a selective opportunity for substituting the expert's default values for less-than-critical questions and so giving a user a result which would otherwise be denied.

Demonstrations of early prototypes to the expert must be heavily qualified by disclaimers of the depth of knowledge. Non-computer experts can easily be over-swayed in their reactions to a system by the quality of the screen displays, particularly the lack of polished graphics. Commenting on the development of the rain penetration system (Chapter 3), Thomson (1986) noted that improving only the graphic display of a window cross-section helped considerably in convincing the experts of the feasibility of the system. We have seen similar reactions to improved graphics. It must also be remembered that any demonstration of an expert system shows only one route through the knowledge base as taken by the searching method when triggered by the particular answers given. It is actually a poor way of looking at the knowledge.

This brings us to method (e) which hinges upon the theme of this book — comprehensibility of the knowledge. The purpose of knowledge elicitation is to extract knowledge, analyse it and represent it for a particular shell. If we can close the loop and put the final knowledge base before the expert for his blessing, we have surely got as close as possible to our objective. Taig (1986), when developing a large expert system to advise engineers on the use of the finite element method, was the expert, the interviewer and the coder — he did it all. This is exceptional, but the author believes we should strive to match that situation. The expert should be entirely happy with the final representation of his knowledge and at least be able to sit down with the interviewer and discuss and criticise it. Case studies could be used to trigger these discussions. Knowledge diagrams (see below) illustrating the links established by the rules between the questions and the goals will help by providing an overall view of the knowledge and will help in these discussions.

We conclude this section by repeating the message that knowledge elicitation and its representation is an iterative process and that steps (b) to (e) will be repeated many times before a well-founded system has been created.

6.5   AIDS TO KNOWLEDGE ELICITATION

The most obvious aid to interviewing is the use of audio or video recorders. They can be intrusive and some experts might react badly to their presence, but a small audio recorder is often quite acceptable. Our experience has been that the time taken to transcribe the tapes later is considerable, and others have reported the same. It can take five to ten hours to transcribe one hour of recording. There is no doubt, however, that stopping an expert in the middle of a train of thought in order to take some written notes is best avoided. We have used two people at interviews: one to take notes, one to ask questions. An audio recorder to act as back-up and help check on specific points later is a good alternative. If this technique is used, the counter on the tape should be noted every 15 minutes to help locate part of the discussion later.

Knowledge diagrams can help experts understand the developing knowledge base, but their production is not easy. Some shells automatically produce a diagram showing all objects and all links between those objects. The objects may or may not be identified by name and, by including all links, the diagram can easily become a nightmarish spider's web. Drawing the diagram by hand — it is best to use a CAD system for this — provides an opportunity to represent some interconnections solely by a text reference, thus reducing the number of lines. Information can be added to help understand the knowledge but it takes much time to draw these diagrams and, of course, they are prone to error and may get out of step with the knowledge base. Their value is greatest where the knowledge base has many intermediate levels and many cross-links. To show the expert all these on one diagram takes advantage of the human eye's ability to scan a picture — missing elements tend to stand out so much more easily than from the printed form. A knowledge diagram has been shown in Fig. 3.1.

Reference has already been made to the use of 'paper models'. If the interviewer is not going to prepare the final knowledge base or if the chosen shell has a knowledge representation form which is not easily comprehended, a neutral intermediate form of the knowledge using the simplest rules can act as a central point of agreement between expert and shell. Of course, there is the risk of error creeping in between the paper model and the final representation, and both need to be kept in step. Having the model version on a word-processing program will make that task easier.

Automatic knowledge acquisition by computer means has been, and remains, a target of AI researchers. In principle, a set of examples must 'contain' some of the knowledge about a topic, and a large enough set will contain it all. Extracting the knowledge is rather more difficult than might be thought. A number of rule induction algorithms have been proposed, and that of Quinlan (1983a) has been embodied in commercially available programs. Our experience of this method was not good in trials on a small sub-section of the dampness expert system. The generated rules omitted facts judged to be important by our expert and were quite different in form from those he helped to develop. We did not have many examples, and others have reported better success with large sets of examples.

A less ambitious but commonly expected version of automatic knowledge acquisition is that of an expert system which 'learns' from its mistakes. In certain on-line control applications, it has been shown that an expert system can modify critical parameters in its knowledge until it has learnt to handle a particular control problem. Extending that idea to expert systems of the type we are discussing may be possible one day, but the author has no knowledge of it now.

Finally, some researchers are developing computer programs to aid knowledge elicitation, and these could play an important role. Kahn *et al.* (1985) describe the program MORE which takes partly formed knowledge and applies eight strategies to it to help probe the expert for more knowledge. Thus, if two goals are linked to the same set of symptoms, the program detects this and probes for new symptoms which would help distinguish them. AQUINAS, developed by Boose (1987), performs a similar role. Clearly, the ideal would be for the resulting knowledge base to be in exactly the form needed by the shell to avoid any re-typing.

7

Knowledge analysis and representation

As set out in Chapter 2, there are two stages involved in representing the knowledge gained from your expert by knowledge elicitation — the analysis of it and its representation in objects and rules. This chapter will expand on the simple ideas expressed earlier by adding a few further remarks about knowledge analysis and by showing the variety of representations in rules and objects adopted by current shells. Attention will be drawn to the advantages of object oriented approaches and, particularly, the use of some 'structure' in collections of objects and rules.

But before considering these matters, this is the appropriate point to emphasize the duality between the knowledge representation and the methods of searching that knowledge. The 'reasoning' ability of an expert system is the sum of *both*. Just as the effective use of BASIC or FORTRAN demands a knowledge of (i) how to write correct statements and (ii) how the computer will act on those statements, so the effective use of a shell hinges upon knowing how to write correct rules and how the shell will make inferences from them. This includes knowing how the searching method works and also how any overall control mechanism works.

Brachman & Levesque (1985) have brought together a splendid collection of key papers on knowledge representation published over the last 30 years, and although these are a challenge to those of us not trained in formal logic, the editors' introduction to each paper opens windows on the possibilities. In their opening introduction they remark 'Simultaneously producing good candidates for each of the three ingredients — the representation language, the inference regime, and the particular domain knowledge — is essentially the central problem of Artificial Intelligence'. Many of the papers in that collection make the same link. At the lower level of AI covered by this book, it still needs the creator of an expert system to understand both the form of knowledge representation and the consequences of the searching methods of a shell. Several examples in this chapter illustrate this point.

This chapter also introduces the topic of structuring objects and rules. Conventional programming languages provide variables for single values (scalars) and variables for sets of values (arrays). The earliest programming languages had only the former type, and it is difficult now to imagine taking such a language seriously.

However, many current expert system shells only offer the comparable facility, i.e. objects which represent a single fact. Some systems allow lists of data items, but they are still treated principally as single entities. One of the most important developments in the last few years is the availability of shells which provide 'frames' roughly equivalent to arrays or rather the structured data form of languages such as PASCAL. The later sections of this chapter will illustrate some of those forms.

There is, unfortunately, no standard for knowledge representation. The pace of development is being set by commercial suppliers of shells; researchers in artificial intelligence are generally more interested in other challenges. Consequently, this chapter reflects the shells the author has used, has evaluated, or has seen. It is perhaps the appropriate place here to comment on the apparent alternative of using either of the popular artificial intelligence languages, PROLOG or LISP, to develop expert systems. Both are important tools for general AI research, but neither has all the facilities needed for an expert system already built in, e.g. robust professional user interfaces, control over searching, uncertainty features, variety of object types, etc. These facilities are provided by modern shells and so enable the creator of a straightforward diagnostic or advice system to concentrate on developing the knowledge base. Both languages have been used to write shells, and LISP, with its low level facilities for processing lists of data items, is very suitable. Many of the larger shells developed in the US are in LISP although most smaller shells are written in conventional programming languages for speed.

Some of the examples in this and later chapters come from the four shells referenced in Appendix 3, SAVOIR, ENVISAGE, LEONARDO and GOLD-WORKS. We have found these to be very useful and powerful but listing them does not mean that they are 'approved', and other examples are influenced by other shells. Shells are reviewed frequently — Allwood (1986) looked at shells available in the UK; Moselhi & Nicholas (1988) reviewed US shells.

7.1 ANALYSIS OF KNOWLEDGE

The basic steps in this task, that of identifying the goals, the preliminary questions and the sub-goals and then writing appropriate rules, were set out in Chapter 2. Two refinements can now be added, both of which spring from the iterative nature of the process of creating an expert system. The identification of appropriate sub-goals may well be modified many times as the knowledge elicitation and analysis reveal more or fewer steps in the reasoning process needed to confirm or deny a particular goal. Whereas it is recommended that the list of final goals be sacrosanct, there is certainly merit in being flexible over the number of sub-goals representing the intermediate steps between the preliminary questions and finding a solution to a problem. First attempts to set down the structure of an expert's knowledge with intermediate stages defined by such sub-goals may well lead to refinement to suggest other sub-goals instead.

This modification of intermediate sub-goals leads to the second refinement. The repeated examination of the knowledge base may yield opportunities to rationalize and 'tighten up' the knowledge representation whenever two or more sub-goals are seen to relate to similar facts. Such a merging of the representation of two intermediate steps may be planned and foreseen by an expert aware of common elements in the diagnosis of two faults. More often, it will represent a small 'flash of light' as such commonality suddenly becomes obvious and all parties wish they had seen it earlier. As an example, in the dampness expert system, the confirmation of a number of causes of dampness such as rising damp, chimney damp, past flooding, etc., depends upon performing a test for the presence or not of salts. Of course, we all should have seen that at the start but, instead, it became obvious only as the knowledge was analysed and represented. The awareness of a common requirement for salt tests then led to the objects and rules about such tests being made more common and consistent across all relevant goals.

We can now summarize the analysis of knowledge in the following way:

(a) Determine as early as possible the goals and preliminary questions.
(b) Analyse the elicited knowledge to determine intermediate steps which form sub-goals.
(c) Prepare a first attempt at suitable objects and rules, taking care to choose names which lead to a comprehensible knowledge base.
(d) Start iterative cycle of refinement involving experts in demonstrations and discussions of the knowledge base, aided by knowledge diagrams and/or paper models.
(e) Be prepared to add/delete intermediate steps in the form of sub-goals and look for the emergence of common sub-goals. Be reluctant to add more final goals.

7.2 VARIATIONS IN RULES

The simple form of rules with propositions linked by AND and with one consequent, as introduced in earlier chapters, is provided by many shells. Most also provide other connectives, principally OR and NOT. The first element of variation comes from the provision or not of brackets and the confusion that can spring from their absence. Here is a rule from the masonry system of Chapter 1 with AND and OR but with no brackets.

> IF cracks are diagonal
> AND crack_appearance is toothed
> OR cracks_at_foundation are obvious
> THEN cause is expansion

What does it mean? If the three propositions are labelled (a), (b) and (c) for conciseness, the rule could be either

> IF (a AND b) OR c THEN d
or   IF a AND (b OR c) THEN d

As a matter of interest, the second is what was meant. If brackets are not provided in a shell, it is advisable to avoid mixing ANDs and ORs in one rule and write two or more rules with the same consequent, e.g.

> IF a AND b THEN d
> IF a AND c THEN d

which together have the same meaning as the second of the two rules above. Even if brackets are provided, the shell may evaluate the rule in a surprising and illogical way. In the first of the bracketed rules above, if proposition (a) is found to be false, there is no point in evaluating proposition (b) — the shell should get on to evaluate proposition (c). At least one shell we have used does not recognize this and asks unnecessary questions to determine the value of (b).

Some shells, including the Simple Shell, provide synonyms for 'equal to' such as IS and ARE — the rule above uses these with obvious benefits to comprehension. The word NOT may be provided as a quite independent operator or may be allowed only in further synonyms, such as IS NOT, ARE NOT, both with the meaning of 'not equal to'. Be careful to note the quite different meaning 'equals' and 'not equals' have when an object can be given one of many meanings, perhaps from a menu. Thus, from the borehole system in Chapter 2, there are three possible answers to the question, 'How would you describe the visibility of separate particles?'.

> Easily seen
> Just discernible
> Not discernible

A proposition such as:

> If separate_particles are not 'easily seen'

does not mean that the particles are 'not discernible'. They could also be 'just discernible'. Whereas a proposition using 'equals' will confirm one particular answer, the negative version simply denies one particular answer.

NOT as an independent operator has an important place in logic, and shells which provide logical variables will certainly allow free use of NOT. However, logical variables raise some problems of comprehension unless used sensitively. Strictly, they should appear in the next section on objects but, because they substitute for propositions in rules, these problems are noted now. Logical variables may be assigned the values TRUE or FALSE as a result of asking a question or evaluating rules. They can appear in other rules substituting for a complete proposition, i.e. not just as an object in a proposition. Thus, we could have a logical variable called

> 'quick_drying_soil'

in place of the object

> 'drying_rate_of_soil' .

It would be given the value TRUE or FALSE according to the answer to the associated question. It would then appear in a rule as

> IF dry_lumps are 'easily powdered'
> AND quick_drying_soil
> THEN soil is probably silt

The negative form of this variable might then appear in a rule such as

> IF dry_lumps are 'broken into smaller lumps'
> AND NOT quick_drying_soil
> THEN soil is probably clay

Awkward forms of such negatives are sometimes difficult to avoid and, to achieve our aim of comprehensibility, must be chosen carefully. Obviously, logical variables are suitable only for facts which are true or false — multi-valued facts cannot be handled by them.

A difficult task in knowledge representation is that of allowing the user to make a graded response, for example from mild to very severe in describing an exposure condition, and then representing that in a readable rule. The easy way is to use numbers and numerical operators which most shells allow, but the rules then become unclear. For example, in the paint selection system described in Chapter 3, a question about wetness at the site of the structure to be painted is put to the user with a numbered menu illustrating increasingly severe environments. This is shown in Fig. 7.1. That is acceptable to the user who only has to select a number and type it in.

```
Please indicate the degree to which the steelwork
    is exposed to moisture as follows:
            (this is not a linear scale)


        Internal dry.....................0
        Internal occasional condensation..1
        Internal moderate condensation....2
        Internal frequent condensation....3
        External sheltered dry...........4
        External sheltered wet...........5
        External fully exposed dry........6
        External fully exposed normal.....7
        External fully exposed wet........8
        Splash zone......................9


    Enter a number between 0 and 9
```

Fig. 7.1 — The wetness_rating question.

However, rules referring to this are reduced to the form

> IF wetness_rating > 3
> ————————
> THEN . . . . . . paint is unsuitable

It is obviously not easy for the expert to remember what severity the constant 3 then stands for. A modest improvement is simply to create objects with an appropriate name to substitute for the constant. For example, if the object 'internal_value' is assigned the value 3, the proposition becomes

IF wetness_rating > internal_value

Some shells such as LEONARDO allow lists of possible answers to be used in propositions along with suitable operators such as INCLUDES. If each wetness rating is now given a short mnemonic and the user allowed to select the appropriate one with a cursor, the proposition could then be in the lengthy but readable form

IF wetness_rating INCLUDES (benign, mild, normal)

An unusual form of rule is adopted in the SAVOIR shell — it follows the pattern used by PROLOG and other logic-based systems by putting the consequent object before the propositions and by not using the words IF and THEN. It also embodies a most interesting feature in the use of 'condition' variables in place of logical variables. These can be given the value of UNKNOWN as well as TRUE or FALSE and, like logical variables, can be substituted for a complete proposition. The consequent object must also be a condition variable. Here is an example taken from the dampness system of Chapter 3 — the rule reflects the expert's suspicion about a defective tiled roof being the cause of dampness in a roof void.

CONDITION tiled_roof_defects
(angle_of_pitch < 16)
OR tile_defects
OR sarking_defects

Its equivalent in the form we have seen before is

IF angle_of_pitch < 16
OR tile_defects ARE 'true'
OR sarking_defects ARE 'true'
THEN tiled_roof_defects ARE 'true'

The condition variables 'tile_defects' and 'sarking_defects' are each evaluated by asking the user a suitable question. (For non-building readers, 'sarking' is the roofing felt or similar material laid underneath the tiles, and the proposition about the angle of pitch shows the expert's deep mistrust of flattish roofs regardless of their condition!) When answering the questions, the user is allowed to reply 'don't know', in which case the associated condition variable is given the value UNKNOWN and the consequent object

'tiled_roof_defects'

is given a value according to a commonsense set of rules. In a nutshell, these rules state that when the elements of a rule are linked only by OR, the consequent object is given the best result from all the elements, i.e. if one is TRUE and the rest are UNKNOWN then the answer is TRUE. When the operator is AND, the consequent object is given the worst result. Brackets can be included to allow ORs and ANDs to be mixed.

This is a first taste of the very important topic of uncertainty in knowledge, or rather uncertainty in a user's response, and will be dealt with in more detail in Chapter 9.

In the construction industry, there is a clear need to allow for situations where a user may or may not be able to answer a question. If the question is merely confirmatory, a failure to answer it may not be fatal but, for key questions, answers may be mandatory. We need ways of handling these situations such as shown above with condition variables.

We conclude this section on rules with a few miscellaneous comments. Some shells allow arithmetic operations in rules or in demons, and this facility is clearly very useful in engineering applications. If such calculations refer to objects not yet evaluated, the normal backward-chaining process is initiated. This can cause some questions to be put in unexpected order unless control of the order of questions has been exerted. Shells which do not allow arithmetic in propositions usually provide a less convenient means of calling a suitable section of conventional programming code to do the work. Some shells allow data to be extracted from a database when an object has to be evaluated. The methods for this are varied and may only employ the facility to call up conventional code as just referred to. Many shells allow more than one consequent action to follow THEN. This is very helpful and does not seem to cause difficulties provided the set of actions form a natural group which should always be performed together.

7.3 OBJECTS

The importance of choosing object names carefully in order to yield comprehensible questions and rules has been aired several times already in this book. We bring together here the points already made, add two more and offer some modest advice to help in thinking of suitable names.

(a) An object's name and the values it can take must make sense when used in propositions with the allowed verbs, usually IS, ARE, IS NOT, ARE NOT.
(b) The values an object takes must make sense to the user if they appear in a menu of answers to a question.
(c) The names should be meaningful when used in any context, i.e. they should be clear and unique and not depend upon adjacency to other object names.
(d) Related objects can be given similar names to highlight the relationship.

Item (c) reflects the global nature of objects. Any object can be used in any rule and its name must be chosen so that it makes sense in all cases. It may be helpful when choosing object names to simply remember that a fact will be described by a noun which may be preceded by adjectives or adjectival nouns or followed by a qualifying clause, e.g.

> (noun)
> wetness_rating
> angle_of_pitch

It is also helpful to consider juggling some of the qualifying words to be used in the propositions from one side to the other of the operator IS (or its synonyms) before choosing an object name. To illustrate the application of these precepts and advice, consider the following rule expressed rather conversationally in Chapter 1 for the masonry example:

> IF the direction of the cracks is vertical
> AND the cracks are widest at the top
> AND there is a single crack on opposite sides of the building
> THEN the likely cause is movement of the ground

In the first proposition the fact being tested is the *direction* of the crack; hence, a suitable representation would be

> crack_direction IS 'vertical'

Similarly, the second proposition could be

> crack_width IS 'widest at top'

Note that in both instances the nouns 'direction' and 'width' representing the appropriate facts were both preceded by the word 'crack' to ensure no possible confusion with other facts which may involve width or direction. The third proposition creates problems by its use of the meaningless word 'there'. The important fact is the presence or not of opposite cracks and so the proposition could be

> single_opposite_cracks ARE 'present'

It will be noted that all the words are linked by underscores so as to eliminate spaces — this avoids the risk of accidentally typing two spaces between words which would create a 'new' object. Many shells do not distinguish between upper and lower case letters and so it is best not to use them.

The manner in which questions are represented in knowledge bases varies greatly, and this is a coding problem which will be illustrated briefly in Chapter 8. It is, however, relevant to this chapter's topic to emphasize the value of questions which are presented to the user with a menu of possible answers rather than simply asking for a yes/no response. Most shells provide built-in facilities for presenting menus easily and with a very professional result appearing on the screen. Apart from their attraction to users, they have real merit within the knowledge representation owing to the high information content such questions carry compared with questions which have simple yes/no responses. In Chapter 3, Fig. 3.2, such a menu question is illustrated for the shape of a dampness stain. Nine possible answers are allowed — admittedly the last is the catch all of 'none of the above'. In answering this question by selecting just one shape, the user will generally cause many rules relating to other shapes to be cancelled, thus rapidly reducing the number of rules left to search. Generally, the user will be asked to select one answer only, but some shells do allow a list of answers to be selected.

We now turn to some aspects concerning consequent objects. Clearly, their names and the values they can take are also governed by the same precepts given above to achieve comprehensibility. There are three further factors to be considered:

(a) Default values.
(b) Positive or negative sense.
(c) Single- or multi-valued.

It can be very useful to be able to arrange for a consequent object, i.e. a goal or a sub-goal, to be given a default value to be used if all rules which referred to that object are proved untrue. Thus, in the paint selection system described in Chapter 3, the expert wished to consider every possible paint as 'suitable' unless the rules for that paint proved it to be 'unsuitable' for the given conditions. How this is provided by shells varies greatly. For example, the LEONARDO shell used for the paint selection system has the facility to associate a set of rules with an object and so can assign a default value to that object if all the associated rules fail. In other shells it may require more specific coding in the rules. This is one use of the ELSE clause provided in some shells. The default value can be set in the *last* rule of a set that refer to the same consequent. It is obviously not very satisfactory to rely on the order of rules in doing this and leads to the risk of creating problems when updating the rule base.

Item (b) referring to the sense of a consequent object can also be illustrated with the same example. The default value was chosen in the positive sense, i.e. 'suitable', simply because there were fewer rules needed to prove a paint was 'unsuitable'. Using the opposite sense would have needlessly increased the number of rules, and it is often worthwhile considering this carefully.

The last item (c) is more difficult, more contentious, and takes us back to the topic of controlling the inferencing sequence of an expert system. The problem may be expressed by using the borehole system of Chapter 2 and was briefly discussed in section 2.3.1. It will be recalled that this system determines which out of 13 classifications best fits a soil sample. We could have used one goal object 'soil' to be given 13 different values according to the rules. Thus, a rule could have ended

THEN soil IS 'clay'

Alternatively, we could (and did) use 13 different goal objects, each of which is given the value 'the correct classification' if the appropriate rules are proved true. The corresponding conclusion is

THEN clay IS 'the correct classification'

The former seems attractive but leads to a single action list — evaluate 'soil'. The sequence of evaluations is then entirely determined (for most shells) by the order of the rules in the knowledge base — the shell simply takes the first rule it finds which refers to soil and, if that fails, the next, etc. To rely on the *order* of the rules in the knowledge base is contrary to the declarative spirit of expert systems and creates unnecessary problems as soon as new rules are added. Some shells do have priority numbers to attach to rules to handle this problem. The second solution of using many specific goals puts control back to the action list or whatever facility is provided for control.

As a final illustration of the need to understand the inferencing and control methods, we can use the example of an incomplete rule set out in section 6.2 to show the need for precise thinking. It is the rule for isosceles triangles. Although this is incomplete, if it were *preceded* in the rule base by a rule for equilateral triangles, it would appear to be correct, and most shells would work successfully with this knowledge base, e.g.

> 1:   IF a = b AND b = c AND c = a
>   THEN triangle IS equilateral
> 2:   IF a = b OR b = c OR c = a
>   THEN triangle IS isosceles

If the rules were reversed, then any equilateral triangle would be declared to be isosceles without even waiting for the length of the third side to be given. Although this example is based on an incomplete rule, it emphasizes the need to think always of the consequences of the inferencing methods — an awareness that will more readily lead to complete and reliable rules.

7.4   STRUCTURED RULES, OBJECTS AND FRAMES

As pointed out before, a proposition such as

> IF crack_direction IS 'vertical'

could be presented to the user in total asking simply whether it is true or not. Separating the object 'crack_direction' from the proposition and asking the user for a value for that object is the first and obvious step in 'structuring' the knowledge base. Immediately, we have the concept of a *question* to get a value for an object and a *proposition* which uses that object. Conventional programming languages make much use of structure, in both data and code, especially in the sense of sub-routines which call other sub-routines. In this section we consider ways in which a few of the more modern shells provide facilities to 'structure' a knowledge base.

The LEONARDO shell allows an object to be associated with a set of rules which lead to a value for that object. These rules can refer to other objects which also may have their own set of rules, etc., etc. The merits of this facility lie in the opportunities provided to 'hide away' sets of rules which relate to one aspect so that they can be either ignored when considering a higher plane of the problem or examined on their own when considering the detailed task they perform. (The analogy to sub-routines or procedures in conventional programming languages will be obvious to programmers.) One simple example of the use of this facility is the task of asking questions and checking the consistency of the answers — one of the steps recommended in Chapter 5 when discussing the likely form of an expert system. The checks and their resulting actions will be represented in a set of rules and, rather than include these with the main rules involved in the central task of diagnosis or offering advice, they can be conveniently parcelled up and tidied away in an object. This can be illustrated by some questions from the paint selection system. An important factor in selecting suitable paints for structural steelwork is whether they are to be applied in a paint shop or outside on site. The answers to this question for primers, barrier coats and finishing coats have to be checked against the answer to a previous question about whether the steelwork is new and not yet erected or does exist and is therefore already erected. The expert applying the consistency checks, emphasized in Chapter 5, wished to give short shrift to any user who tried to take 'existing' steel back to the paintshop, but to give only a strong warning message to a user who wished to apply finishes to 'new' steelwork in a paintshop and, therefore, risk scratching during erection. In these and other checks, rules are needed which force a question to be re-asked or display a message. Rather than have all these in the main rule set cluttering up the real knowledge, they could, in the LEONARDO shell, be coded one level down in a suitable object. For example, for the primers we could have the object

> where_primer_painted_checked

and within its rule set would appear the basic question of where the primer was to be painted and all the consistency rules with their messages and actions. Only when all checks had been satisfactorily made would the object above be set to its value of 'done' and the main rule set allowed to continue its work.

A more powerful extension of structuring of the knowledge base is loosely analogous to the provision of arrays in conventional languages or, better still, the data structures and records of PASCAL or database systems. The concept of representing a situation by taking a suitable basic 'chunk' of knowledge and then adapting and adding to that to represent each specific situation was first introduced by Minsky (1975). He described this as a framework for knowledge representation, and the term 'frames' has come to mean groups of facts, rules and other data which fall into classes. Minsky also introduced the terminology 'slots' to refer to the items of knowledge which make up the frame. To give substance to this idea, we illustrate part of the paint selection expert system which uses frames as provided by the LEONARDO shell to represent the knowledge about the four components of a paint scheme, i.e. surface treatment, primer, barrier and finish coats. Fig. 7.2 shows the structure for the class of frames representing the finish coats. The top level class frame contains the names of all the potential paints for the finish, each of which has a member frame at the first level down. The top level class frame could contain data values which would be 'inherited' by all members of the class — in fact, this feature was not used. Each member frame represents a different paint with appropriate data values for cost, life, thickness, etc., and also with its own set of rules about the suitability or not of that paint acting as a finish coat. An example of a frame for a surface treatment appears in Fig. 3.3. The complete set of frames can then be referred to by one rule, such as that given in Fig. 7.3 which ensures that all possible finish paints are examined in turn. (In the paint selection system, it was necessary to examine all components in four nested rules.) This rule starts with the phrase 'for all finish' which is quite comprehensible if not grammatically correct. It forces the system to re-apply the rule to each frame in the class 'finish', clearing the rule each time. A useful alternative is 'for some ———' which stops at the first frame which satisfies the rule. Fig. 7.3 also shows the neat and comprehensible references to data slots within the rule, e.g. 'value: of primer', 'cost: of barrier', etc.

CLASS

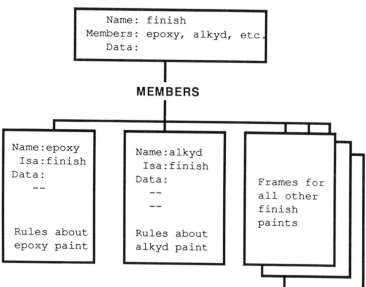

Fig. 7.2 — Frames for paint selection system.

```
for all finish

        IF value: of finish is 'suitable'
        AND value: of primer is 'suitable'
        AND value: of barrier is 'suitable'
        AND value: of surface_treatment is 'suitable'
        AND thickness_criteria are 'acceptable'
            etc.

  THEN paint_scheme is 'acceptable';
        cost = cost: of surface_treatment +
        cost: of primer + cost: of barrier +
        cost: of finish
```

Fig. 7.3 — A LEONARD rule operating on frames.

Other modern shells currently available take this concept further and provide multiple levels of frames, each of which can inherit knowledge from one or more higher level frames. Frames can also be created at run time and may have many data slots whose values can be derived at run time. The GOLDWORKS shell provides such facilities, and one can develop with it a 'lattice' in which frames connect to 'parent' and 'child' frames. This is especially useful where there are complex physical or organizational relationships between objects. As an engineering example one could use a set of frames to store data about the beams, columns and slabs of a building. The beams could be part of a hierarchy, along with the slabs, representing the floors of the building and also part of a hierarchy, along with the columns, representing the vertical structures of the building. Rules to operate on a floor or on a structure could extract data from the same beam frame.

The syntax of rules for GOLDWORKS is less clear than for LEONARDO but provides great flexibility. It uses the concept of 'pattern-matching'. Any fact established by the user answering a question, defined as such by the system or created as the consequence of a rule, is held in a list of 'assertions' as a set of words or symbols. Each bracketed element of a rule is used as a template to see if any assertion(s) match it. If so that element is taken to be true and the next element is examined. The flexibility comes from allowing variables to be substituted for part of an element — if the rest of the element matches up to an assertion, the variable is associated (bound) to the remainder of the assertion for the purpose of the current rule only. The use of the same variable in two or more elements of a rule provides a very powerful facility. As an illustration, the paint selection rule shown in Fig. 7.3 is repeated in GOLDWORKS form in Fig. 7.4. It will be seen that the very readable

```
IF  (INSTANCE ?F IS finish
         with value suitable
         with cost ?fcost)

AND (INSTANCE ?P IS primer
         with value suitable
         with cost ?pcost)

AND (INSTANCE ?B IS barrier
         with value suitable
         with cost ?bcost)

AND (INSTANCE ?S IS surface_treatment
         with value suitable
         with cost ?stcost)

AND (thickness_criteria are acceptable)
         etc.

THEN
     (paint_scheme is acceptable)

AND (cost = stcost+pcost+bcost+fcost)
```

Fig. 7.4 — The GOLDWORKS equivalent of Fig. 7.3.

phrases such as 'value: of ———' are replaced by a quite long winded equivalent. That is the cost of the increased power of pattern matching with variables.

8

Coding, testing, and verifying

8.1 CODING

The knowledge base must be coded in its final form according to the syntax of the chosen shell. If the knowledge representation of the shell is comprehensible, the coding may well go hand-in-hand with the knowledge analysis and representation. Most knowledge bases can be prepared by a general editor or word-processing program — some shells have their own editors built in.

Care is needed in this work because of the global nature of the elements of the knowledge base. Despite the caveats of the preceding chapter, the rules of a knowledge base do not have to be in order. That, however, is not an invitation to create total disorder. Computer scientists are rightly scathing of large BASIC programs developed in piecemeal fashion with liberal GO TO statements joining up last minute additions to ill-thought out starters. A large knowledge base can easily attain the same spaghetti-like form. The shell program may still be able to search through it, but humans will find that very difficult to do. All the exhortation for comprehensibility of rules will be lost if they are not grouped and ordered in some way to reflect facets of the reasoning.

Some overall form or pattern should therefore be imposed on the knowledge base. Most shells allow harmless comments to be inserted in the knowledge base — use them to indicate the form. A simple form could be:

(a) preliminary questions and associated consistency rules;
(b) intermediate sub-goals with their rules;
(c) final goals and main rules.

The reverse would do just as well. Adopting one or other or some different but quite deliberate structure is a big step to maintaining comprehensibility and attaining an error-free knowledge base. The importance of this is a pointer to the type of person needed to do this work — a neat, tidy worker with a good memory may be better than the fast-thinking but sloppy whiz kid.

The consistency that comes from an overall structure to the knowledge base can be extended to the propositions themselves. Rules are more easily understood if the order of objects in propositions and the order of propositions is the same in rules which use the same elements. Thus, a proposition such as

IF cost>target_cost

should not become, in another rule,

IF target_cost<cost

This just creates unnecessary mental gymnastics. Similarly, if lists of objects appear in the knowledge base, stick to the same order on each appearance if at all possible.

Many shells allow a descriptive label to be associated with each rule — it may only appear in the print out or it may be displayed to the user on command. If some rules have come from a technical note or a code of practice, this label can be used to refer to the source and so aid the self-documentation of the knowledge base.

8.1.1 Coding questions, explanations, and displays

The syntax of how a question is actually coded for a knowledge base varies from shell to shell, but Fig. 8.1 illustrates the form used in the LEONARDO shell for a yes/no

```
 1:            Name: toughness_needed



 9:   Allowedvalue: no,yes


13:   Queryprompt: Put the cursor on the appropriate
14:                response and press return
15: Querypreface: Will the paint scheme be subjected
16:                to knocks and abrasions in use ?
17:     Expansion: Polyurethane top coats, epoxy
18:                barriers, primers and finishes,
19:                zinc silicate primers and
20:                galvanizing all yield tough
21:                paint schemes
```

Fig. 8.1 — Coding of a LEONARDO question.

question. The text to be displayed to the user follows the commands on lines 13 to 15, and line 9 defines the acceptable range of the answer (the missing lines are not relevant to this display). This figure also illustrates one way of providing supplementary text to assist a user answer a question. The text on and after line 17 is displayed if the user presses the f7 function key. Most shells provide similar features.

It is important when phrasing such explanatory text to think carefully about the future users of the expert system. Their likely experience, knowledge of the topic, and familiarity with the related jargon must be correctly judged or the explanatory text may be above their comprehension or judged to be trivial. A similar problem must be faced when planning explanatory texts to be used when answering the user's question 'why?'. As mentioned earlier, some shells show the rules themselves when answering this question, some allow 'canned text' attached to a rule to be displayed. The same strictures about thinking of potential users clearly apply when choosing such text, but there is another consideration. If a hierarchy of several layers of rules is being evaluated when the user asks 'why?', the explanatory texts associated with each rule must make sense when displayed altogether as some shells do. Even if a shell displays only the text of the 'current' rule, it is likely to allow repeated use of 'why?' to penetrate through the hierarchy, thus exposing each explanation. Clearly, any inconsistency or contradictions in the explanations will be non-user-friendly.

Providing displays to keep the user informed about the progress of a diagnosis is one of the recommended stages in a user-friendly system set out in Chapter 5. Coding these displays will generally be by demons, i.e. rules which have as a consequent not an object but an action. The action will be to display some text on the screen, and most shells have provision for such demons. Devising rules to put intermediate displays on the screen will only be worthwhile in large, and therefore long-running, systems, but they make a real contribution to acceptability. Clearly, shells which allow several consequents to follow THEN make it simple to cause a suitable display to appear as soon as an important sub-goal has been successfully evaluated.

One problem in achieving this is of being sure that the shell will display the message as soon as the conditions in the rule are established as true. Some shells do not work as one might expect and so cause difficulties here, but these problems are ones of testing and so are left to the next section.

8.2   TESTING

The robustness of a well-proven shell coupled to the freedom of rule order makes it disarmingly simple to get an expert system running very quickly indeed and with a very professional appearance. The contrast with the usual extended birth of a conventional program can create a false impression of an immediately tested system. It is, of course, not the case. Indeed, the searching strategy of shells produces a problem of a terrifyingly large number of possible 'routes' through a knowledge base. A careful analysis of the rules in the dampness system produced an estimate of well over 20 000 possible combinations of answers all leading to a sensible result — and this from only 171 rules. This is an illustration of the combinatorial explosion once thought to be a barrier to expert systems' progress, but now solved by modern searching methods. It remains still a problem for humans testing an expert system. As with conventional programs, there are a few steps one can take to eliminate the 'silly' errors before starting a test programme. Many shells make a check on the syntax of the knowledge base before attempting to execute it, and this stage is often part of a compilation process designed to produce fast execution. Clearly, such shells will pick up simple errors made in key words, and some shells go a long way towards checking that the object and constants in propositions are of matching types.

Shells usually produce lists of the names of objects referred to in the rules. From experience, we have found it to be well worthwhile spending time examining such a list before embarking upon tests. Typing errors may well cause extra unwanted objects to appear, and spotting those at an early stage can save much time. For a simple knowledge base, having the list in an alphabetic order can make it easier to spot the rogue names, but, for a larger knowledge base where groups of related objects have been defined together in frames, alphabetic ordering can destroy an otherwise useful adjacency. Of course, an entirely object-oriented approach to creating the knowledge base, as exemplified by the Simple Shell, avoids this type of error.

It is usually quite easy to commence testing on a small part of a knowledge base, perhaps one goal or even one sub-goal. A temporary action list, as shown in section 2.4, to evaluate only one or two objects can be used to test one part of a large knowledge base without any other surgery. If a new shell is being used, this is the opportunity to become familiar with its working method. It is very good practice to follow either the knowledge base itself or a knowledge diagram and check that the shell asks each question in the order you expect. This is not easy with many rules being triggered, but tackling it with a sub-set of the knowledge base that relates to just one sub-goal will keep the problem in scale. One particular problem can be mentioned here again. It concerns the manner in which shells update the knowledge base as each object is evaluated, i.e. how, or rather when, the opportunistic forward-chaining is deployed. In principle, this should be immediately an object gets a value, but some shells delay updating until the rule currently being considered is finished with. This can cause unnecessary questions to be asked but, more critically, can hold up demons which are ready to trigger some action, particularly that of displaying messages to the user. A firm understanding of how the shell works may help find ways round such problems.

Having tested all parts of a knowledge base by the device of evaluating one object at a time, testing of the full system can commence. Clearly, the best material for this is a set of case studies of past problems provided by the expert, but you should take care to use straightforward test cases with clearcut answers. This is the stage of iterative improvement of the knowledge base and it is to be expected that the test problems will help refine the knowledge as well as find errors in the knowledge representation. There is no need to complicate this process by tackling problems which could defeat the expert.

The potential users of the expert system should not be forgotten in this testing phase. Their ability to understand the text of questions, of messages and even the results, is all part of the iterative refinement of the knowledge base. Involving the users in this work is also an excellent way of motivating their enthusiasm for its eventual introduction. Indeed a formal evaluation by users could parallel the verification stage to be discussed next, and it should never be forgotten that the utility of any program hinges on the user's answer to the question 'Is it worth the trouble?'.

Many shells provide some 'trace' facilities to help track the route taken through the questions. Even a simple screen dump will create a printed record of a test run, but it is better if the shell provides a facility to log the complete consultation on a disc file for a later print out. If a test run produces an unexpected and possibly wrong answer, it is as well to have a reliable record of that run. It is remarkably easy to get confused about which set of answers led to which result unless a record is kept. Some shells allow a run to stop part way through and to save all appropriate values on a disc file. Re-starting from that point and then trying different answers to later questions is an efficient way of testing many combinations.

8.3 VERIFICATION

Bearing in mind the enormous number of possible routes through a knowledge base, it is unrealistic to believe that a knowledge base can ever be fully tested. In addition, we have to face the likelihood that the knowledge base will not contain *all* our expert's knowledge on the chosen topic and the possibility that our expert is himself not infallible. Put together, that appears to yield a statement that we cannot produce a totally reliable expert system. But do we expect human experts to be infallible? Of course not; only nearly infallible! What is needed is to verify our expert system to gain confidence in it to the same extent as we have in our expert.

How can we do that? How would we test a new human expert? Putting those two questions together raises the possibility of employing the famous test devised in 1950 by the brilliant Alan Turing — can the computer be distinguished from a human if both respond only through a keyboard and a screen? O'Keefe *et al.* (1987), in one of the few papers on this topic of verification, report that some medical expert systems have been verified that way — that is by blind comparisons of the results of trials on both the expert system and on known experts. Such comparisons eliminate the known bias people have towards or against computers.

We are still left with the task of selecting a suitable set of trial problems and be sure we know the right answers to them. This is certainly difficult, and O'Keefe appears to argue that they should reflect the distribution of problems in real life, i.e. that if some causes are very common, then most problems should be set to test those causes. This is certainly the easiest way, since producing such trials only requires looking up sufficient past case studies. But is this how we would test a new human expert? Surely we would want to talk to him, to probe his knowledge generally and then try him out with a few standard problems and a few difficult problems. The analogous approach to verifying an expert system would then seem to be:

(a) Get all available experts to examine the knowledge base (with knowledge diagrams to aid their understanding of it).
(b) Put to the expert system a number of real problems exploring the less common as well as the usual cases.
(c) Put the same problems to other experts.
(d) Make a blind comparison of the results obtained from (b) and (c).

In making that comparison, it could well be that some cases have arguable results, and further explorations will have to be made in order to confirm the true diagnosis.

Clearly, verification is a task which will increase greatly with the size of an expert system knowledge base, but we should keep it in perspective. For the straightforward diagnosis and advice systems we are considering in this book, a combination of careful testing as set out in section 8.2 and the verification process given above should yield a satisfactory level of confidence in the system.

9

Uncertainty

Whilst there is some agreement over how to represent knowledge concerning deterministic problems — our virtually exclusive concern so far in this book — there is wide diversity about representing and handling knowledge of uncertain problems. This is unfortunate. Practical problems are full of uncertainty and nowhere more so than in the construction industry. However, there are some methods and several commercially available shells embody one or more of them.

Firstly, let us be clear about two sorts of uncertainty:

(a) uncertainty in a user's response to a question, and
(b) uncertainty in the link between a proposition and a consequent.

A user may not always be able to answer a question with a definite 'yes' or 'no'. This has been alluded to already in section 7.2 where the possibility of allowing the user to respond 'don't know' was raised. This is an important provision. If a user is asked whether there are defects in parts of a building which are difficult to access, the answers 'yes', 'no', and 'don't know' all convey different meanings which should be allowed for in the knowledge representation. Some shells invite the user to go another step and give a graded numerical response, typically -5 to $+5$, to represent all shades of view from 'no' to 'yes'. When this is coupled to numerical means of incorporating the graded response into the likelihood of a rule being true or not, it would seem that we have a very sophisticated and powerful tool. Quite apart from the doubtful validity of the numerical methods (to be discussed), the author doubts the consistency with which any two people would interpret intermediate answers on this scale. Thus, in considering condensation as a cause of dampness, one might ask the question:

> 'Is the air in the room humid? -5 to $+5$'

What would the answer -3 mean? Would the responses of different individuals be consistent? It seems very unlikely. Apart from illustrating one consequence of the numerical processing of such answers, we shall not consider this type of response again, and the author firmly believes and recommends in sticking to 'yes', 'no', and 'don't know'.

Uncertainty when answering a menu question is a different matter. In many circumstances where a user is expected to choose one response out of a menu, he may find that difficult. A good example is again from the dampness system where the user is shown a list of nine types of stain shape to choose from (Fig. 3.2). Users typically want to select several shapes. It is not difficult to handle this where shells allow answers to be lists, in which case the propositions can use the verb INCLUDES rather than IS to allow for the choice made by the user.

Our main topic is that of uncertainty in the knowledge, even if the user's responses are quite unambiguous. It is not simply that the presence of one symptom may only partly confirm a cause; more important and more difficult is to allow that whilst two symptoms are mildly indicative on their own, when seen together the indication of a particular cause positively leaps up. Since we shall refer to this phenomenon more than once in this chapter, here is an example taken again from the dampness expert system as described in section 3.1. Condensation as the cause of damp stains on a wall may be confirmed by:

(a) stains which match structural elements behind the wall (therefore acting as a thermal sink);
(b) humid air conditions in the room.

Separately, either will have only a small effect on the probability that condensation is the cause — if they appear together, condensation is almost a certainty. How these effects are to be represented is the challenge.

A challenge not to be discussed, but not to be overlooked either, is whether uncertainty represents ignorance that could be replaced by knowledge. Perhaps most uncertainty is truly non-determinable, but it could just be worth considering whether some study would reveal knowledge to bridge the gap.

Pang *et al.* (1987) in a recent survey reported on nine different methods of representing uncertainty — there are certainly more. We shall consider four main types:

(a) Linguistic, i.e. the use of words such as 'likely'.
(b) Extended logic.
(c) Single probabilities.
(d) Upper and lower bound probabilities.

9.1 LINGUISTIC METHODS

Some writers (and the suppliers of shells with no provision for uncertainty) argue that it can all be done with ordinary rules and the right choice of words, e.g.

>   IF shape_of_stain IS 'similar to structural elements'
>   THEN cause_of_dampness IS probably condensation

This raises immediately the problem of whether everyone will interpret words such as 'probably', 'could be', etc., in the same way. In a cold conversation with a computer, that is very unlikely. We use these words in conversation in very variable senses according to our own judgement of the experience the listener has in the topic concerned. No such feedback and automatic adjustment takes place in the computer.

There is another problem in this approach which stems from the non-linear combination effect shown by the example which ended the introductory section above. With two symptoms, it would be necessary to write four separate rules covering all combinations (assuming only 'yes' and 'no' answers) to give different strengths to the conclusion. With three symptoms, it would be nine rules, etc. This is a combinatorial explosion which must be avoided — it is, by the numerical methods which follow.

9.2 EXTENDED LOGIC

We have raised above the possibility of allowing a user to answer 'don't know' to a question as well as 'yes' or 'no'. It is straightforward to define the results of the logical operators AND and OR on two objects which may each take the values 'yes', 'no', 'unknown'. Table 9.1, which is derived from the SAVOIR manual, shows the results. The value of allowing a user to answer 'don't know' has been emphasized above, but it can be seen from Table 9.1 how often 'unknown' will be the result of logical operators and, therefore, of a rule. Further, in a hierarchy of rules one answer of 'don't know' could easily lead to a number of unsatisfactory conclusions of 'unknown'.

The SAVOIR shell, which calls these objects condition variables, provides a very useful means of linking them to the single probability value representation of uncertainty, which we are about to consider in the next section, and which to some extent gets over this problem. The link is a function to convert a condition variable to a corresponding probability — 'yes' becomes 1, 'no' becomes 0 and 'unknown' becomes 0.5 or some other defined value. This conversion is quite consistent within the limitations of a single probability value and has proved a very useful way of allowing a user to say 'don't know' but to process the result more sensitively than have it swamp a large part of a knowledge base by just using the logical operators of Table 9.1.

9.3 SINGLE PROBABILITY VALUE

We are used to relating probabilities to statistical analyses of many tests, and we know that the probability of a tossed coin coming down heads may be confirmed as 0.5 by performing many tests. In general, we do not have the opportunity to do the number of tests necessary to determine the probabilities we want for our construction industry expert systems — but we can, instead, talk of the probability as 'a measure of belief'. It makes perfectly good sense to say:

> IF I toss up a coin
> THEN, with a measure of belief of 0.5, it will come down heads

This is on a scale where 0 = I do not believe it will happen, 1 = I am certain it will happen.

Table 9.1 — Extended logic operators AND OR

A \ B	yes	unknown	no
yes	Y	U	N
unknown	U	U	N
no	N	N	N

Result of **A AND B**

A \ B	yes	unknown	no
yes	Y	Y	Y
unknown	Y	U	U
no	Y	U	N

Result of **A OR B**

We can now consider assigning such measures of belief to the potential goals of our expert system and modifying those values as symptoms are observed. There are three methods in use in commercially available shells: certainty factors as used in the earliest medical expert system MYCIN (Shortliffe, 1976), the Bayes theorem, and fuzzy logic. The author has used the latter two only in the SAVOIR shell and reports on those here.

9.3.1 Bayes' theorem
The Revd Thomas Bayes (1702–1761) developed a method for modifying the probability of a hypothesis as evidence about it accumulated, and his theorem has become important in modern decision theory. The mathematics can be reduced to the following:

If a hypothesis has a probability p
    before a piece of evidence a is considered
then its probability p' when evidence a is found to be true
    is modified by a weighting factor w and becomes

$$p' = \frac{p.w}{(p.w+1-p)}$$

This looks rather inconvenient, but if the probabilities p and p' are expressed as odds o and o' instead by the conversion

$$o = \frac{p}{(1-p)}$$

then Bayes' theorem reduces to the simple formula

$$o' = o.w$$

Note that a weighting factor w of 1 causes no change in the probability, i.e. it means that the presence or not of evidence a is immaterial.

    Strictly, the weighting factor can be calculated from two conditional probabilities, but these are very difficult to derive. If we use the example of condensation and stain shape given above, then, to calculate the weighting factor appropriate to stains of the right shape, we need the two probabilities of:

(a) the stains occurring if condensation is the cause, and
(b) the stains occurring if condensation is *not* the cause.

Neither of these values is likely to be available or easily judged by the expert and so we have adopted a method of deriving the weighting factors directly.

    Before we look at that method, there are a few matters to be discussed, and this is best done with an example of how Bayes' theorem is implemented in a shell. The form adopted by the ENVISAGE shell is most clear, and for our condensation example could be expressed as:

```
condensation DEPENDS ON
stain_is_shape_of_structural_element AFFIRM a DENIES b
air_is_humid                         AFFIRM c DENIES d
PRIOR q
```

In this statement the letters a, b, c, d, and q stand for numerical constants yet to be determined. The object 'condensation' starts with the probability q before the user is asked questions about the stain shape and the humidity. His answer can be 'yes', 'no', or 'don't know'.

    The first problem is what is an appropriate starting value q for the probability of condensation being the cause of dampness before any evidence is considered. In the absence of any data, we assume $q=0.5$ corresponding to 'don't know'. Whether it is reasonable to assign 0.5 in cases of ignorance is one of the criticisms made of Bayes' theorem. Secondly, it will be noted that each proposition has two weighting factors, identified in the shell ENVISAGE by the words AFFIRMS and DENIES. The first factor is used if the proposition is proved true, the second if the proposition is proved false, and a value of one is used if the proposition is unknown. The two factors are quite independent and represent two separate applications of Bayes' theorem. Further, contrary to many people's assertions, either factor can be greater or less than one. In our example, the affirmatory factors a and c are likely to be greater than one since the two propositions are both phrased positively to confirm the likelihood of condensation. It is, however, perfectly acceptable to have a proposition which, if proved true, would reduce the probability of condensation. As an example, we could include in the above statement a proposition depending upon the result of a test for moisture in the interior of the wall, e.g.

> moisture_in_wall_is_high AFFIRM 0.1 DENIES 1

Confirmation of this proposition would tend to suggest that the cause of dampness is water penetrating through the wall, not condensation, and so the affirmative weighting factor is less than one.

As an aside, the author records his distaste for the commonly used alternatives to AFFIRMS and DENIES, namely LS and LN. These are abbreviations for 'logical sufficiency' and 'logical necessity' which imply unnecessary meaning to two simple weighting factors.

We now come to a difficulty with the Bayes method which needs careful attention. The statement given above has two propositions which both influence the final probability. It is a strength of Bayes' theorem that it can handle any number of pieces of evidence and they can be taken in any order, BUT they must be *independent* of each other. There is no doubt in our example that shape of stain and humidity are quite independent factors. It is not easy to guarantee this in all statements in a knowledge base, particularly if the propositions are sub-goals of rules, and there is a risk of two sub-goals depending upon the answer to the same question.

Finally, before turning to the task of estimating the weighting factors, it should be noted that an expert system shell will process a Bayesian knowledge statement in a manner different from a rule. Not all propositions in a rule may need to be evaluated — if one is proved false and the rest are linked only by AND, the rule is proved false and the remaining propositions can be left unevaluated. Not so with a Bayes statement. All propositions must be evaluated before the final probability is known. Indeed, some shells such as SAVOIR take advantage of this and store a maximum and minimum probability for each goal derived by calculating the best and worst possible result before starting a consultation and then updating these, by the Bayes theorem, as well as the current estimate of the probability. The values converge for a goal when the last relevant proposition is evaluated.

9.3.2 Deriving Bayes weighting factors

A pragmatic approach we have used (Allwood *et al.*, 1988) is to prepare sets of theoretical case studies of the most likely combinations of evidence and put these to the expert for his assessment of the final probabilities. Table 9.2 shows the four cases for the example above with the expert's opinion of the probability that condensation

Table 9.2 — Case studies for Bayes weighting factors

PROPOSITIONS	Case 1	Case 2	Case 3	Case 4
stain_is_shape_of_ structural_element	N	Y	N	Y
air_is_humid	N	N	Y	Y
Expert's judgement of condensation being the cause ---- probability	0.05	0.4	0.6	0.95
----------- odds	0.05	0.67	1.5	19.0

would prove to be the cause in each case. The last line of the table gives the equivalent of the probabilities in odds. Since the prior probability q has been assumed to be 0.5, equivalent to odds of 1, Bayes' formula can now be applied for each of the four cases, yielding the following equations for the weighting factors:

$$b.d = 0.053 \qquad \text{solution} \quad a = 3.5$$
$$a.d = 0.67 \qquad\qquad\qquad b = 0.28$$
$$b.c = 1.5 \qquad\qquad\qquad c = 5.4$$
$$a.c = 19.0 \qquad\qquad\qquad d = 0.19$$

The rounded values given for the weighting factors yield the desired probabilities estimated by the expert — note the way in which, when the two propositions are present, the probability is very high; whereas if only one is present, the probability remains little altered.

These equations cannot always be solved. If there are more propositions and if 'unknown' is to be allowed for as well as 'yes' and 'no', the number of cases increases greatly. We have found it worthwhile to write a simple program to allow weighting factors to be derived on a trial and error basis so as to match all predicted cases and not produce unreasonable probabilities for all other cases. The general rule is to use weighting factors as close to one as possible. It goes without saying that the resulting weights must be discussed with the expert, since their relative values must coincide with his own views of the importance of each proposition.

9.3.3 Interpolating a graded response by a user
Some dangers of allowing a user to respond on a scale of −5 to +5 were outlined above. Since several shells allow this response and then incorporate it into the Bayes method by unjustified means, a further warning is sounded. Since +5 corresponds to 'yes' which causes the positive weighting factor to be used and 0 corresponds to 'don't know' which effectively leads to a weighting factor of 1 to be used, it is easy to see the attraction of a simple linear interpolation for all other values between 0 and +5.

Equally, all values between 0 and −5 can be interpolated between 1 and the negative weighting factor. Such linear interpolation is provided in some shells and leads to a false, but remarkably rosy, result. Consider a statement such as the following where the second proposition — the test for moisture inside a wall — is a counter indicator for condensation. Note the two propositions have equal weights but in opposite senses.

Condensation DEPENDS ON
air_is_humid   AFFIRMS 5 DENIES 0.2
wall_interior_is_damp   AFFIRMS 0.2 DENIES 5
PRIOR 0.5

As you would expect, and can verify, two 'yes' or two 'no' answers cancel each other out and yield a probability of 0.5. Not so with two partial 'yes' answers represented by +3 and +3. The resulting probability is 0.64. More surprisingly, −3 and −3 give the same result. Non-linear interpolations can be and are used to restore symmetry, but there is no justification for any of them. If you are tempted to use graded responses in a shell, do try the above test first.

9.3.4 Fuzzy logic

Extended logic (section 9.2) operates on 'yes', 'don't know', and 'no' corresponding to probabilities of 1.0, 0.5 and 0. It is natural to consider whether there are ways of defining how AND and OR can operate on variables with any value of probability. This has led to the notion of fuzzy logic with suitable operations which coincide with ordinary logic when probability values of 1.0 and 0.0 are used. There is some argument over the appropriate formula for intermediate values. A common set, which at first sight looks the wrong way round, is

probability of (A AND B) = minimum of probability of A
                           or probability of B

probability of (A OR B) = maximum of probability of A
                          or probability of B

Some alternatives are a more pessimistic AND obtained from the product of the probabilities of A and B and a more optimistic OR being the smallest of either 1.0 or the sum of the two probabilities.

It has been reported many times that fuzzy logic formulae such as these, when implemented as part of an inferencing scheme, tend to produce probabilities which are very near to one or zero. We have however found the formulae for AND and OR natural to use in conjunction with Bayesian statements. For example, there are several ways in which rain can penetrate into a building — through the roof, through the walls, through the window frames. In the dampness system, these are represented by separate sub-goals each with a Bayesian statement. The fuzzy formula MAX (corresponding to OR) was used to select the greatest of the resulting probabilities to yield the most likely cause of the rain penetration.

9.4 UPPER AND LOWER PROBABILITY BOUNDS

The obvious weakness in using a single value of probability or measure of belief is that we are unlikely to know the value accurately — indeed, that could only be the case if we were able to perform a large number of tests under controlled conditions. It is more natural to expect an expert when asked for a probability value to say, 'It will be between x and y'. The gap between the values tells us something about the confidence the expert has in that judgement. Thus, in case 4 of Table 9.2, the expert might well have given a range of 0.9 to 1.0 for the probability of condensation because of the significance of having the two indicators acting together. Case 3 could well have led to a wider band, say 0.5–0.7. In this last reply, the expert is saying that,

the probability of the cause being condensation is at least 0.5 and
the probability of the cause NOT being condensation is at least $(1-0.7) =$ 0.3.

The second is sometimes an easier way to find a suitable upper value.

Several writers, e.g. Shafer (1976), Quinlan (1983b), and Blockley (1987), have proposed methods for inferencing with such uncertainty bounds often based on the work of Dempster (1967). The author has no experience of using shells with these bounds, and no commercially available shell with this facility is known to him. Although bounds have an instinctive appeal and one can expect to see shells appearing with appropriate inferencing methods, a stout defence for single probability values has been mounted by Cheeseman (1985). He questions the utility of a pair of bounds and draws an analogy with the use of a single concentrated mass at a point to satisfactorily represent a distributed mass in many problems of mechanics.

10

The future of expert systems in the construction industry

Expert systems, as described in this book, represent the application of artificial intelligence research that is at least 10–15 years old. It may well take another 5–10 years before the present technology, perhaps a little more polished as practical usage exposes some rough edges, is exploited by industry. What can we see from more recent research to provide hints of the future? Before attempting to answer that question, it is worth remarking on a paradox in AI which may mean that the current systems will be the future systems. Advanced research in AI is concerned, amongst many other matters, with how to represent and process knowledge about fundamental laws, e.g. of gravity, of mechanics, of thermo-dynamics, etc., in a way which can be easily included in expert systems of all types including those we have looked at. The rules of the dampness expert system BREDAMP incorporate gravity, seepage, heat transfer, etc., but in rules which relate to specific instances of these phenomena. How much easier to have that already built in to the system. But is it possible and, more to the point, will we be able to understand how to use it when it is done? There is a circular argument here in that the nearer AI gets to representing human intelligence the more difficulty we humans will have in understanding how to use it — after all, we do not know how our own brains work despite years of effort. It could be that, unless there is a breakthrough, this will mean that we take only very modest steps forward from the technology of rules, objects, and frames already available. This is an unusual situation. Finite element and computer aided drawing programs needed much user-driven development before the early research tools became production tools. The user-driven development of expert systems may impact more on the periphery of the technology than on the basics.

10.1 SOME LIKELY DEVELOPMENTS

The developments in hardware that will affect our use of expert systems are easy to see. There will be faster, more powerful, more portable micro-computers which will run our shell software very well. Better communications by networks will help and, as in most areas of computer usage now, hardware will not be a problem. The software developments are much more difficult to see, not least for the argument raised above. Some, which are the subjects of current development, are:

(a) integration of shells with other software,
(b) knowledge representation of graphics,
(c) message passing,
(d) the 'blackboard' concept, and,
(e) uncertainty.

Most shells provide a means of communicating with data bases, spread sheets, or other stand-alone programs. The methods are usually crude and cumbersome and we clearly need a more radical approach if we are to integrate expert systems with our current range of software tools. Perhaps we need a new kind of supervisory or organizing software — a program which sits 'above' all the different modules for data bases, graphics, calculations and expert systems, and which handles all communications between the modules and all arguments over which module has the next turn. The role of project manager might be a template.

The most urgent need is undoubtedly that for representing 3-D graphical information in a knowledge base. We need to be able to pass 3-D CAD models of buildings or structures to expert systems and, with suitable operators, get answers to questions such as, 'What is above this room?', 'What objects intersect this space?', etc. Research in this field is under way — but it is a very big subject.

The searching processes described in this book can be seen as methods which pass single facts through a knowledge base and work out the consequences stemming from that fact. Passing a message of several data items around instead is now quite an old idea but not yet in much use. A message of just several facts would be no improvement — the message must contain different data as well. One simple possibility is that of constructing as a message an object name; the value of that object; and the measure of belief in that value. It is not difficult to envisage improved knowledge statements which hinge upon the presence of an object with a value which is known with a certain measure of belief.

The 'blackboard' concept is a jargon for collecting together the results of several attempts to solve a problem by different means, e.g. by different inferencing methods and knowledge. It was introduced by researchers working on such topics as hand-writing recognition where several methods of recognizing letters have been devised and are used in parallel. It is difficult to see this becoming useful in engineering applications except, perhaps, in design. In diagnosis, there may be alternative confirmatory tests but, most commonly, there will be one main line of reasoning.

Uncertainty has been discussed in Chapter 9 and the likelihood was raised there of commercially available shells offering upper and lower probability bounds as a method of handling uncertainty. This hinges upon identifying a commonly acceptable method, but the research community interested in this topic is small and will remain so until users start demanding improved methods.

10.2   SOME FUTURE ADVANTAGES OF EXPERT SYSTEMS

The immediate and obvious advantages of expert systems have been mentioned already — ready availability on the site or in the office; users cannot skip critical questions; an alternative method of recording knowledge compared with books and reports; explanations given to the users. It is possible to guess at further advantages to be seen only when expert systems are in established use. As tools for the dissemination of knowledge, they have the potential to be more easily updated than the printed page. This will be particularly true where distribution of a knowledge base can be by a network and be entirely computer based. Sending out floppy discs by post will not be so easy, but at least the user will not have to tear out and replace individual pages in the company standards book every month or so. The acceptability of expert systems by engineers in an office will hinge on their perception of its value, but there is the advantage that consulting an expert system in the privacy of an office is far less embarrassing than facing a formidable expert. Being foolish in private is acceptable to us all. There is also a clear indication already that frequent consultation of an expert system is itself a useful if sub-conscious learning process which could be of great value to junior staff.

10.3   SOME FUTURE PROBLEMS INCLUDING MARKETING AND RESPONSIBILITY

We must be constantly aware of the impact expert systems will have on people, not just on the immediate users but all affected by the advice given. Diaper (1988) gives a useful indication of the potential extent of that influence. We must also be aware of the need to constantly verify a knowledge base as it develops and most expert systems are likely to continue to develop. We should view a knowledge base much as we do a code of practice and change it with care.

Chapter 1 concluded with the comment that knowledge is a commercial asset and so expert systems embodying an organization's knowledge might not come on to the market as readily as conventional programs have done. It is a commonly repeated view that the larger commercial corporations have clamped down on publications about their work in expert systems for fear of helping competitors. In the construction industry it may be seen to be a good thing to demonstrate publicly an up-to-date approach by the use of expert systems. But will that extend to releasing all the knowledge in an expert system as it would be if it were sold? Clearly, publicly funded bodies with a commitment to disseminating information to the construction industry will see this as a new vehicle to complement reports and data sheets. Private firms may not want to sell their 'know how' except at a price.

The consequent risk of legal liability for negligence in the advice offered by an expert system could well be a further deterrent. Zeide & Liebowitz (1987) offer an American view that 'expert systems haven't experienced much legal trouble yet, but great litigious potential exists over their use, misuse and non-use (a potential that will soon be realized)'. That could be interpreted as a lawyer's anticipation, but it leads to a clear conclusion to this book. Expert systems are a new technology which may not be available off the shelf. Those organizations which learn to use the technology will gain an advantage in the future.

References

d'Agapeyeff, A. and Hawkins, C. J. B. (1987) Corrosion Prediction. *Report to the ALVEY Directorate on the Second Short Survey of Expert Systems in UK Business, Appendix C*, D.T.I., London.

Allwood, R. J. (1986) Using expert system shells. *Int. J. of Construction Management and Technology,* **1** No. 3, 23–36.

Allwood, R. J., Shaw, M. R., Smith, J. L., Stewart, D. J. and Trimble, E. G. (1988) Building dampness: diagnosing the causes. *Building Research and Practice,* **16** No. 1, 37–42.

Atkinson, N. (1987) The desktop gurus. *Process Eng.* October pp. 33–34.

Berry, D. C. and Broadbent, D. E. (1986,1987) Expert systems and the man–machine interface. *Expert Systems* **3** No. 4, 228–231, 1986, and **4** No.1, 18–26, 1987.

Bijl, A., Stone, D. and Rosenthal, D. (1979) *Integrated CAD Systems.* EdCaad, Edinburgh University.

Blockley, D. I. (1987) Uncertainty analysis in expert systems. *Civ. Engngn. Syst.* **4**, March pp. 3–6.

Boose, J. (1987) AQUINAS: A knowledge acquisition workbench for building knowledge-based systems. In Addis, T. *et al.* (eds.) *Proc. First European Workshop on Knowledge Acquisition.*

Bowen, J. A., Cornick, T. C. and Bull, S. P. (1986) BERT — An expert system for brickwork design. *University of Reading*, England.

Brachman, R. J. and Levesque, H. J. (eds.) (1985) *Readings in knowledge representation*, Morgan Kaufmann Publishers Inc.

Brandon, P. S., Basden, A., Stockley, J. and Hamilton, I. (1988) *Expert systems and strategic planning of construction projects*, RICS, London.

BS 5390:(1981) *Site Investigation.* British Standards Institution.

Cheeseman, P. (1985) In defence of probability. In: Joshi, A. (ed.) *Proc. 9th Int. Jt. Conf. on Artificial Intelligence*, pp. 1002–1009.

Cooper, C. N. (1987) CRANES — A rule-based assistant with graphics for construction planning engineers. *CIVIL-COMP 87, The Application of Artificial Intelligence Techniques to Civil and Structural Engineering*, CIVIL-COMP PRESS, Edinburgh.

Dempster, A. P. (1967) Upper and lower probabilities induced by a multivalued mapping. *The Annals of Mathematical Statistics,* **38** No. 2, 325–339.

Diaper, D. (1986) Will expert systems be safe? In: *Second Int. Expert Systems Conf.,* 561–572, Learned Information, Oxford.

Diaper, D. (1988) The promise of POMESS. In: *Proc. of Human and Organizational Issues of Expert Systems,* Stratford, England.

Diekmann, J. E. and Kruppenbacher, T. A. (1984) Claims analysis and computer reasoning. *J. of Construction Eng. and Man.,* **110**, No. 4, ASCE, 391–408.

Dym, L., Henchey, R. P., Delis, E. A. and Gonick, S. (1988) A knowledge-based system for automated architectural code checking. *Computer-aided-design,* **20** No. 3, 137–145.

Eldridge, H. J. (1976) *Common defects in buildings.* H.M.S.O., London.

Hamilton, G. and Harrison, A. (1986) *Expert systems for the construction and building services industry,* Tech. Note TN 7/86, BSRIA.

Hosking, J. G., Mugridge, W. B. and Buis, M. (1987) FireCode: a case study in the application of expert systems techniques to a design code, *Planning and Design* **14**, 267–280.

Jacobs, D. A. H. (1987) Expert systems related to electricity generation. *Civ. Engng. Syst.* **4** 8–11.

Kahn, G., Nowlan, S. and McDermott, J. (1985) MORE: An intelligent knowledge acquisition tool. *Proc. 9th Int. Jt. Conf. on Artificial Intelligence,* Los Angeles, pp. 581–584.

Lansdown, J. (1982) *Expert Systems,* RIBA, London.

Levitt, R. E. and Kunz, J. C. (1987) Using artificial intelligence techniques to support project management. *AI EDAM,* **1**, 3–24.

Maser, K. R. (1986) Automated interpretation of sensor data for evaluating in-situ conditions. *Proc. First Int. Conf. Applications of Artificial Intelligence in Engineering Problems,* pp. 861–886.

Michie, D. and Johnston, R. (1984) *The Creative Computer,* Viking.

Minsky, M. (1975) A framework for representing knowledge. In: Winston. P. (ed.) *The Psychology of Computer Vision,* McGraw-Hill, NY pp. 211–277.

Moselhi, O. and Nicholas, M. J. (1988) Expert system tools for construction planning and control. *Microcomputers in Civil Eng.* **3**, No. 1, 75–80.

Naylor, C. How to build an inferencing engine. In: Forsyth, R. (ed.) (1984) *Expert systems: Principles and case studies.* Chapman and Hall.

Nilsson, N. J. (1980) *Principles of Artificial Intelligence,* Tioga Publishing Co.

O'Keefe, R. M., Balci, O. and Smith, E. P. (1987) Validating expert system performance. *IEEE EXPERT,* Winter 1987, pp. 81–90.

Palmer, R. N. and Tull, R. M. (1987) Expert system for drought management planning. *J. of Computing in Civil Eng.,* **1** No. 4, ASCE, 284–297.

Pang, D., Bigham, J. and Namdani, E. H. (1987) *Reasoning with uncertain information,* ALVEY project, Queen Mary College, London.

Quinlan, J. R. (1983a) In: *Machine Learning: An Artificial Intelligence Approach.* Michalski, R. S., Carbonell, J. G., Mitchell, T. M. (eds.), Tioga Publishing Corp. 1983, p. 463.

Quinlan, J. R. (1983b) Inferno: A cautious approach to uncertain inference. *The Computer J.,* **26**, No. 3, 255–269.

Reinschmidt, K. F. and Finn, G. A. (1986) Applications of expert systems in engineering, design and construction. Stone & Webster Engineering Corp., Boston, USA.

Rosenman, M. A., Gero, J. S. and Oxman, R. (1986) An expert system for design codes and design rules. *Proc. First Int. Conf. Applications of Artificial Intelligence in Engineering Problems, Southampton University*, Springer-Verlag. pp. 745–758.

Shafer,G. (1976) *A mathematical theory of evidence*, Princeton University Press, NJ.

Sharpe, R. and Aldham, W. (1988) Electron beam welder expert system development. *Proc. Symp. on Knowledge-based Systems in Civil Engineering*, Monash University.

Shaw, M. R. (1986) Applying expert systems to environmental management and control problems. Building Research Establishment.

Shortliffe, E. H. (1976) *Computer-Based Medical Consultations: MYCIN*, Elsevier/North Holland, NY.

Taig, I. C. (1986) Expert aids to finite element system applications. *Proc. First Int. Conf. Applications of Artificial Intelligence in Engineering Problems, Southampton University*, Springer-Verlag pp. 759–770.

Thomson, J. V. (1986) A water penetration expert system using prolog with graphics. *Proc. 2nd Australian Conf. of Expert Systems*, New South Wales Institute of Technology, Sydney, May 1986, pp. 51–73.

Thomson, J. V., Delaney, J., Marksjo, B., Sharpe, R., Grant, A., Raimondi, D. and Prior, M. (1987) An expert system to give advice to operators of a metropolitan water supply, drainage and sewerage network. *Proc. Australian Jt. Artificial Intelligence Conf.*, Sydney.

Tommelein, I. D., Levitt, R. E. and Hayes-Roth, B. (1987) Using expert systems for the layout of temporary facilities on construction sites. *CIB W-65 Symposium, London*.

Trethowan, H.A. (1987) The knowledge base — Will the frog turn into a prince? *Reprint No. 60.*, Building Research Association of New Zealand.

Zeide, J. S. and Liebowitz, J. (1987) Using expert systems: the legal perspective. *IEEE EXPERT*, pp. 19–21.

Appendix 1 — The Simple Shell

1.1 PURPOSE

This shell has two particular features — it can, if wished, display a 'commentary' on its inferencing process to help a user learn more easily how the searching methods work. It also requires that the objects of the knowledge base be defined before rules can be created, i.e. it is object oriented. Written in BASIC, its capacity and speed are limited, but knowledge bases of up to 40 or 50 rules are easily handled. The propositions can be quite sophisticated, it has demons and control of inferencing is by an action list. Output can be directed to a printer if desired. The program is written in Microsoft BASIC and runs on an IBM compatible PC. It is available on XT format discs for a handling charge of £10 ($20) from:

> Dr R. J. Allwood,
> Department of Civil Engineering,
> University of Technology,
> Loughborough,
> Leics. LE11 3TU,
> England.

1.2 GENERAL OPERATING INSTRUCTIONS

The BASIC interpreter on your computer must first be entered; then, after inserting the shell disc in the drive, enter the command

> CHAIN "SSHELL"

The program starts by displaying the main menu as follows:

> 1 LOAD KNOWLEDGE BASE
> 2 SAVE KNOWLEDGE BASE
> 3 DISPLAY/EDIT OBJECTS
> 4 DISPLAY/EDIT RULES

    5 DISPLAY/EDIT ACTIONS
    6 RUN EXPERT SYSTEM
    7 COMMENTARY ON/OFF
    8 SWITCH OUTPUT TO SCREEN/PRINTER
    9 LEAVE SSHELL

You control the program from this menu and from sub-menus which appear when appropriate. Your input, WHICH MUST ALWAYS BE COMPLETED BY PRESSING RETURN, will be:

(a) a number to select a main menu or a sub-menu option,
(b) a letter to select a sub-menu option when the display includes letters in brackets,
(c) numeric or text data.

1.3 INPUT OF OBJECTS, RULES AND ACTIONS

As set out above, you must define your OBJECTS first and then create RULES. If you have a printer, a listing of your objects makes the second stage easier. Lastly, you define the ACTION list, and the knowledge base can then be executed. All elements of the knowledge base can be edited and stored on a disc. The input is described below, using a few objects and a rule from the Borehole example as an illustration.

1.3.1 Input of objects

Select Main Menu option 3 and you will see a display of any objects already created and the following sub-menu:

    SELECT: (N)EW, (O)VERWRITE, (M)AIN MENU

Typing one of the bracketed letters causes one of the following actions:

    N — define a new object
    O — overwrite an old object
    M — return to Main Menu

If (O)VERWRITE is selected, you must give the number of the object to be overwritten: the program then follows the sequence given in Fig. 1 for a (N)EW object. In Fig. 1, the user's input is ringed. Some general comments on the input of objects can be made. If the names of objects have separate words, these can be joined by '_' as shown — this is needed by some shells and so used here. If a goal or sub-goal is defined (types 1 and 2), no question text is asked for. If a question object is defined (type 3), up to five possible answers are allowed. If a number object is defined (type 4), an upper and lower limit are asked for and these are used to check the user's input at run time.

    Each time an object is added or overwritten, the full set is displayed on the

```
WHAT IS THE NAME OF THE OBJECT ?
```

dry_lumps

```
INPUT 1 FOR GOAL, 2 FOR SUB-GOAL, 3 FOR QUESTION
                  4 FOR NUMBER
```

3

```
WHAT IS THE TEXT FOR THE QUESTION ?
```

How would you describe the way a dry lump
of soil crumbled between the fingers?

```
HOW MANY POSSIBLE ANSWERS WILL THIS OBJECT HAVE ?
```

3

```
ANSWER 1 ?
```

easily disintegrated

```
ANSWER 2 ?
```

easily powdered

```
ANSWER 3 ?
```

broken into smaller lumps

```
OBJECT No.   NAME AND POSSIBLE ANSWERS
    1        dry_lumps  easily disintegrated
                        easily powdered
                        broken into smaller lumps
```

User's input is ringed

Fig. 1 — Input and display of object.

screen. This can be printed by selecting Main Menu option 8 to switch the display from the screen to printer. This should be re-set to the screen after use. It is a safe practice to SAVE your objects on the disc before using them for rules.

1.3.2 Input of rules
Rules cannot be created until all relevant objects have been specified. It is best, if possible, to have these printed out as shown below:

OBJECT NUMBER	NAME AND POSSIBLE ANSWERS	
1	dry_lumps	easily disintegrated
		easily powdered
		broken into smaller lumps
2	separate_particles	easily seen
		just discernible
		not discernible
3	soil	sand
		probably silt
		probably clay

Select Main Menu option 4 and you will see a display of all existing rules and then the same sub-menu as used in objects.

SELECT: (N)EW, (O)VERWRITE, (M)AIN MENU

Typing one of the bracketed letters leads to one of the following actions:

N — define a new rule
O — overwrite or alter an existing rule
M — return to Main Menu

Rules for the simple shell can have up to four propositions connected by AND. If OR is needed, write two rules instead. Each proposition can have the form of:

object	operator	constant	or
object	operator	object	

All elements of the proposition are selected by numbers: the objects from the list of defined objects, the operators from a set of eight shown on the screen, the constant from the list of possible answers given when defining the selected object.

Fig. 2 illustrates the sequence used for creating the first proposition of the rule shown below. The user's input in that figure is ringed.

IF   dry_lumps ARE easily disintegrated
AND   separate_particles ARE easily seen
THEN   soil IS sand

The rule appears on the screen in the form above after it is defined. After inputting the last proposition, the program offers a choice of consequent. It is at this stage that *ASK or *DISPLAY can be chosen to create demons. The full list of rules may be printed out using Main Menu option 8 to switch from screen to printer and the rules should also be saved with option 2 when they are created.

If the (O)VERWRITE option is chosen, there is a further sub-menu allowing the whole rule to be overwritten, one proposition only to be overwritten or a new proposition to be added.

```
PROPOSITION 1
WHAT IS THE NUMBER OF THE OBJECT?
```

```
OBJECT SELECTED IS dry_lumps
IS THIS CORRECT (Y/N) ?
```

```
SELECT AN OPERATOR BY NUMBER
        1 =
        2 <
        3 >
        4 <>
        5 IS
        6 IS NOT
        7 ARE
        8 ARE NOT
```

```
(C)ONSTANT OR (O)BJECT?
```

```
SELECT A CONSTANT BY NUMBER

        1 easily disintegrated
        2 easily powdered
        3 broken into smaller lumps
```

```
IS THERE ANOTHER PROPOSITION (Y/N) ?
```

```
        User's input is  ringed
```

Fig. 2 — Input of a proposition.

1.3.3   Input of actions

Main Menu option 5 allows you to create the ACTION list of objects to be evaluated in order. The objects can be questions, numerical questions, or goals in any order. Creating them follows the same pattern as for rules, i.e. by selection from the object list. The action list can be edited and printed and is stored on disc with the rest of the knowledge base using Main Menu option 2.

1.4   EXECUTING A KNOWLEDGE BASE — WITH OR WITHOUT COMMENTARY

The whole knowledge base of objects, rules, and action list should be loaded from the disc with Main Menu option 1 and then executed with option 6. Questions will appear with menus of possible answers or with numeric ranges which will be checked. If a conclusion is reached, this will be displayed; if not, a message to that effect appears.

Main Menu option 7 allows you to switch on or off a running commentary of the actions of the shell. This has been provided to help users learn how the shell searches through the knowledge. It is also very helpful if a knowledge base does not appear to be working correctly. The commentary normally appears on the screen, but it can be directed to the printer with option 8. In that case, the questions still appear on the screen.

1.5   GENERAL PROGRAM DETAILS — INCLUDING RECURSION

The program is listed in Appendix 2. It has REMARK statements preceding each of its many sub-routines; the main ones correspond to the three flow charts of Chapter 4. Sub-routine 4000 controls the execution of the knowledge base, sub-routine 4500 evaluates an object and sub-routine 6000 evaluates a rule. The data structures are set out in section 1.6. These arrays are all dimensioned by the variable Z which can be re-set on line 10 to use up whatever space for BASIC variables your computer has less an amount for character strings. The value set is suitable for the usual 64K limitation and allows up to 40 rules. It will be noted that the evaluation routines use few FOR loops. This is because many of the loops have to be left before completion and most BASIC interpreters do not like programs which do that — hence, IF statements are used.

Recursion is not provided in most BASICs but is not difficult to program. It occurs in the Simple Shell when the sub-routine for evaluating an object has to be entered from the sub-routine for evaluating a rule. This can happen many times until an object is successfully evaluated. What needs to be preserved at this stage are:

> the key variables such as the number of the current rule and current object
> the address the sub-routine is currently intending to return to

The former can easily be stored in arrays with an increasing counter. These arrays all start with the letters STK to indicate that they are 'stacks' — computer jargon for arrays used for this purpose. The latter means that ordinary sub-routines ending with RETURN cannot be used since the line number to go to when that statement is reached is hidden away. Instead, we use:

> ON x GO TO n1, n2, etc.

making sure that the list of line numbers n1, n2, etc. includes all possible return addresses. In the object sub-routine, the variable x is RTOB; in the rule sub-routine, the variable is RTRL. The values of these variables must also be put on to a stack array. Sub-routines 6300 and 6320 do most of the work.

1.6 DATA STRUCTURES

1.6.1 Objects

NOBJS   = no. of defined objects

Each has an entry in the following arrays.

TYP$( )	= G,SG,Q,N — type of object
NAM$( )	= name of object
QTXT$( )	= question text (if type Q or N)
POSS$(,$p$)	= up to five possible values (p=1,5)
QSTAT$( )	= ANS or UNK — whether answered or not
RES$( )	= result

In addition, this array is created at the start of execution

RULE(,p) = rules which refer to this object (p=1,8)

1.6.2 Rules

NRULS = no. of defined rules

Each has an entry in the following arrays

for proposition p=1,4

NUM(,p)	= no. of first object
OP(,p)	= no. of operator
CON$(,$p$)	= constant or *object no.
PSTAT$(,$p$)	= T,F or UNK — status of proposition p
RSTAT$( )	= T,F or UNK — status of rule
RTYP$( )	= G,SG,*ASK,*DISPLAY — type of consequent
CNUM( )	= no. of consequent object
CRES$( )	= result or text for *DISPLAY

1.6.3 Actions

NACTS = no. of defined actions

Each has an entry in the array

ACT( ) = no. of object to be evaluated

1.6.4 Recursion

NTOB	= no. of times subroutine 4500 entered recursively
NTRL	= no. of times subroutine 6000 entered recursively
STKN( )	= stack of object nos. being evaluated
STKJ( )	= stack of rule nos. being evaluated.

Appendix 2 — Listing of Simple Shell

```
1 REM SSHELL VERSION1.0, RJALLWOOD JULY 1988
10 Z=50
15 DEV$="SCRN:"
20 NOBJS=0:NRULS=0:NACTS=0:PR=0
30 DIM TYP$(Z),NAM$(Z),QTXT$(Z),POSS$(Z,6),QSTAT$(Z),RES$(Z),RULE(Z,8),
NRL(Z)
40 DIM NUM(Z,5),OP(Z,4),CON$(Z,4),PSTAT$(Z,4)
50 DIM RSTAT$(Z),RTYP$(Z),CNUM(Z),CRES$(Z)
60 DIM ACT(Z),STKN(5),RETOBJ(5),STKNJ(5),RETRUL(5)
65 DIM STKI(5),STKJ(5),STKA$(5)
70 DIM OPR$(10),OBTYP$(4),CONTYP$(4)
71 FOR I=1 TO 10:READ OPR$(I):NEXT I
72 DATA =,<,>,<>,IS,IS NOT,ARE,ARE NOT,<=,>=
73 FOR I=1 TO 4:READ OBTYP$(I):NEXT I
74 DATA G,SG,Q,N
75 FOR I=1 TO 4:READ CONTYP$(I):NEXT I
76 DATA G,SG,*ASK,*DISPLAY
80 GOSUB 250
90 ZZ$="SELECT: (N)EW, (O)VERWRITE, (M)AIN MENU"
99 OPEN DEV$ FOR OUTPUT AS #1
100 CLS
110 PRINT SPC(20),"PLEASE SELECT AN OPTION"
115 PRINT
120 PRINT SPC(20),"1.   LOAD KNOWLEDGE BASE"
130 PRINT SPC(20),"2.   SAVE KNOWLEDGE BASE"
140 PRINT SPC(20),"3.   DISPLAY/EDIT OBJECTS"
150 PRINT SPC(20),"4.   DISPLAY/EDIT RULES"
160 PRINT SPC(20),"5.   DISPLAY/EDIT ACTIONS"
170 PRINT SPC(20),"6.   RUN EXPERT SYSTEM"
175 PRINT SPC(20),"7.   COMMENTARY ON/OFF"
177 PRINT SPC(20),"8.   SWITCH OUTPUT TO SCREEN/PRINTER"
178 PRINT SPC(20),"9.   LEAVE SSHELL"
180 PRINT :INPUT "   NO. OF YOUR OPTION ",N
185 PRINT
188 IF N=9 THEN STOP
190 IF N>8 OR N<1 GOTO 100
199 ON N GOTO 400,300,600,800,1000,4000,500,520
200 INPUT"PRESS RETURN TO CONTINUE ",A$:RETURN
250 REM CLEAR
255 FOR I= 1 TO Z
260 TYP$(I)=" ":NAM$(I)=" ":RTYP$(I)=" "
265 NEXT I:RETURN
300 REM WRITE KB TO DISC
315 INPUT"INPUT THE FILE NAME OR (M)AIN MENU ",A$
316 IF A$="M" OR A$="m" GOTO 100
320 CH=2:OPEN A$ FOR OUTPUT AS #2
```

```
325 INPUT"GIVE A SHORT DESCRIPTION OF THE KNOWLEDGE BASE   ";A$
330 WRITE #CH,A$,NOBJS,NRULS,NACTS
335 FOR I=1 TO NOBJS
340 WRITE #CH,TYP$(I),NAM$(I),QTXT$(I)
345 FOR J=1 TO 5:WRITE #CH,POSS$(I,J):NEXT J
350 NEXT I
355 FOR I=1 TO NRULS
360 FOR J= 1 TO 4:WRITE #CH,NUM(I,J),OP(I,J),CON$(I,J):NEXT J
365 WRITE #CH,RTYP$(I),CNUM(I),CRES$(I)
370 NEXT I
375 FOR I=1 TO NACTS:WRITE #CH,ACT(I):NEXT I
390 CLOSE #CH
399 GOTO 100
400 REM READ KB FROM DISC
415 INPUT"INPUT THE FILE NAME OR (M)AIN MENU ",A$
416 IF A$="M" OR A$="m" GOTO 100
420 CH=2:ON ERROR GOTO 550:OPEN A$ FOR INPUT AS #2
425 ON ERROR GOTO 0
430 INPUT #CH,A$,NOBJS,NRULS,NACTS
435 FOR I=1 TO NOBJS
440 INPUT #CH,TYP$(I),NAM$(I),QTXT$(I)
445 FOR J=1 TO 5:INPUT #CH,POSS$(I,J):NEXT J
450 NEXT I
455 FOR I=1 TO NRULS
460 FOR J= 1 TO 4:INPUT #CH,NUM(I,J),OP(I,J),CON$(I,J):NEXT J
465 INPUT #CH,RTYP$(I),CNUM(I),CRES$(I)
470 NEXT I
475 FOR I=1 TO NACTS:INPUT #CH,ACT(I):NEXT I
480 PRINT "DESCRIPTION OF KNOWLEDGE BASE":PRINT A$
490 CLOSE #CH
499 GOSUB 200:GOTO 100
500 CLS:INPUT"1 = ON, 0 = OFF ",PR:GOTO 100
520 CLS: PRINT "INPUT S FOR SCREEN, P FOR PRINTER"
525 INPUT A$: IF A$="S" OR  A$="s" THEN DEV$="SCRN:":CLOSE #1: GOTO 99
530 IF A$="P" OR A$="p" THEN DEV$="LPT1:":CLOSE #1: GOTO 99
535 GOTO 520
550 REM ERROR HANDLING
555 IF ERR=64 OR ERR=53 THEN PRINT "FILE NOT FOUND"
580 RESUME 415
590 GOTO 100
600 REM INPUT AND DISPLAY OBJECTS
605 IF NOBJS=0 GOTO 620
610 PRINT #1, "      OBJECTS":PRINT #1,
615 FOR N=1 TO NOBJS:GOSUB 1800:NEXT N
620 PRINT #1, :PRINT ZZ$:INPUT A$
625 IF A$="M" OR A$="m" GOTO 100
630 IF A$="O" OR A$= "o" THEN INPUT "INPUT NUMBER OF OBJECT TO OVERWRITE   "
;N:GOSUB 1800:GOTO 652
640 IF A$<>"N" AND A$<>"n" GOTO 620
650 IF NOBJS=Z THEN PRINT #1, "NO MORE OBJECTS ALLOWED":GOTO 620
652 IF N<1 OR N>NOBJS GOTO 620
654 IF TYP$(N)<>"N" THEN INPUT "DO YOU WANT TO (O)VERWRITE THE OBJECT OR
(C)HANGE ONE ANSWER?   ",A$
656 IF A$="C" THEN INPUT "INPUT NO. OF ANSWER TO CHANGE   ",I:INPUT "NEW ANS
WER   ",POSS$(N,I):GOTO 770
658 GOTO 670
660 NOBJS=NOBJS+1:N=NOBJS
670 INPUT"WHAT IS THE NAME OF THE OBJECT?   ",NAM$(N)
680 PRINT "WHAT TYPE OF OBJECT IS IT?"
681 PRINT"INPUT 1 FOR GOAL, 2 FOR SUB-GOAL,"
682 PRINT"         3 FOR QUESTION, 4 FOR NUMERICAL QUESTION "
683 INPUT M: IF M>4 OR M<0 GOTO 683
685 TYP$(N)=OBTYP$(M)
690 IF M<3 GOTO 705
700 INPUT"WHAT IS THE TEXT FOR THE QUESTION?   ",QTXT$(N)
702 IF M=4 GOTO 750
705 INPUT"HOW MANY POSSIBLE ANSWERS WILL THIS OBJECT HAVE? (MAX 5) ",M:
IF M>5 OR M<1 GOTO 705
710 FOR I=1 TO 6:POSS$(N,I)="":NEXT I
720 FOR I=1 TO M:PRINT #1, "ANSWER    ";I:INPUT POSS$(N,I):NEXT I
730 GOTO 770
```

```
750 INPUT"UPPER LIMIT?   ",POSS$(N,1)
760 INPUT"LOWER LIMIT?   ",POSS$(N,2)
770 GOSUB 1800: GOTO 620
800 REM INPUT AND DISPLAY RULES
805 IF NRULS=0 GOTO 820
810 PRINT #1, "RULES":PRINT #1,
815 FOR N=1 TO NRULS:GOSUB 2000:NEXT N
820 PRINT :PRINT ZZ$:INPUT A$
830 IF A$="M" OR A$="m" GOTO 100
835 IF A$="O" OR A$= "o" THEN INPUT"INPUT NUMBER OF RULE TO OVERWRITE ",N:G
OSUB 2000:GOTO 880
840 IF A$<>"N" AND A$<>"n" GOTO 820
845 IF NRULS=Z THEN PRINT "NO MORE RULES ALLOWED":GOTO 820
850 NRULS=NRULS+1:N=NRULS:GOTO 900
880 INPUT"DO YOU WANT TO (O)VERWRITE THE RULE COMPLETELY, ALTER OR ADD A
(P)ROPOSITION OR A (C)ONSEQUENT OR Q)UIT?  ",A$
890 IF A$="P" OR A$="p" THEN INPUT"NO. OF OLD OR NEW PROPOSITION? ";I:GOSU
B 3000:GOTO 980
892 IF A$="O" OR A$="o" THEN GOSUB  3100:GOTO 980
895 IF A$="C" OR A$="c" GOTO 910
899 GOTO 820
900 FOR I=1 TO 4:NUM(N,I)=0:OP(N,I)=0:CON$(N,I)="":NEXT I:GOSUB 3100
910 PRINT "SELECT A TYPE OF CONSEQUENT BY NUMBER"
915 FOR I=1 TO 4:PRINT I;"    ";CONTYP$(I):NEXT I
920 INPUT M:IF M<1 OR M>4 GOTO 920
925 RTYP$(N)=CONTYP$(M)
930 ON M GOTO 940,940,960,970
940 INPUT"WHAT IS THE NUMBER OF THE CONSEQUENT OBJECT? ",I
941 IF I<1 OR I>NOBJS GOTO 940
942 IF TYP$(I)<>"G" AND TYP$(I)<>"SG" THEN PRINT "NOT A GOAL OR SUB-GOAL
OBJECT":GOTO 940
945 PRINT "SELECT A RESULT BY NUMBER":J=1
950 PRINT J;"     ";POSS$(I,J)
952 IF POSS$(I,J+1)<>"" THEN J=J+1:GOTO 950
955 INPUT K:IF K>J OR K<1 GOTO 955
957 CNUM(N)=I:CRES$(N)=POSS$(I,K):GOTO 980
960 INPUT"WHAT IS THE NUMBER OF THE QUESTION OBJECT?  ",CNUM(N):GOTO 980
970 INPUT"WHAT IS THE TEXT TO BE DISPLAYED?  ",CRES$(N)
980 GOSUB 2000:GOTO 820
1000 REM INPUT AND DISPLAY ACTIONS
1005 IF NACTS=0 GOTO 1020
1010 PRINT #1, "ACTION NO. ","OBJECT NO,":PRINT #1,
1015 FOR I=1 TO NACTS:PRINT #1, I,ACT(I),NAM$(ACT(I)):NEXT I
1020 PRINT ZZ$:INPUT A$
1025 IF A$="M" OR A$="m" GOTO 100
1030 IF A$="O" OR A$= "o" THEN INPUT"INPUT NUMBER OF ACTION TO OVERWRITE   "
;N:GOTO 1080
1035 IF A$<>"N" AND A$<>"n" GOTO 1020
1040 IF NACTS=Z THEN PRINT "NO MORE ACTIONS ALLOWED":GOTO 1020
1050 NACTS=NACTS+1:N=NACTS
1080 INPUT"WHAT IS THE NUMBER OF THE OBJECT   ";M
1085 IF M>NOBJS THEN PRINT "OBJECT DOES NOT EXIST":GOTO 1080
1090 ACT(N)=M:PRINT #1,I,M,NAM$(M)
1099 GOTO 1020
1800 REM DISPLAY OBJECT N
1810 PRINT #1,N, NAM$(N)
1820 I=1:IF QTXT$(N)<>"" THEN PRINT #1,SPC(10); QTXT$(N)
1830 PRINT #1, SPC(20),POSS$(N,I)
1840 I=I+1:IF POSS$(N,I)<>"" GOTO 1830
1850 PRINT #1,:RETURN
2000 REM DISPLAY RULE N IN FULL
2010 A$="IF   ":B$=STR$(N):I=1
2015 C$=CON$(N,I):IF ASC(C$)=42 THEN M=VAL(MID$(C$,2)):C$=NAM$(M)
2020 PRINT #1, B$,A$;NAM$(NUM(N,I));"  ";OPR$(OP(N,I));"  ";C$
2030 A$="AND ":B$=" ":I=I+1
2040 IF NUM(N,I)<>0 GOTO 2015
2050 A$="THEN  "
2060 IF RTYP$(N)="*DISPLAY"THEN PRINT #1,"  ", A$;"*DISPLAY  ";CRES$(N):
PRINT #1,:GOTO 2090
2070 IF RTYP$(N)="*ASK" THEN PRINT #1,"  ", A$;"*ASK ";NAM$(CNUM(N)):PRINT
#1,:GOTO 2090
```

```
2080 PRINT #1, "    ",A$;NAM$(CNUM(N));" IS    ";CRES$(N):PRINT #1,
2090 RETURN
3000 REM INPUT PROPOSITION I IN RULE N
3020 GOSUB 3200: NUM(N,I)=M
3030 PRINT "SELECT AN OPERATOR BY NUMBER"
3035 FOR J=1 TO 9 STEP 2
3040 PRINT ,J;"    ";OPR$(J),(J+1);"    ";OPR$(J+1):NEXT J
3041 INPUT K:IF K>10 GOTO 3041
3045 OP(N,I)=K:IF TYP$(M)="N" GOTO 3080
3050 PRINT "SELECT A CONSTANT BY NUMBER OR (O)BJECT":J=1
3055 PRINT J;"    ";POSS$(M,J)
3060 IF POSS$(M,J+1)<>"" THEN J=J+1:GOTO 3055
3065 INPUT A$:IF A$="O" OR A$= "o" THEN GOSUB 3200:CON$(N,I)="*"+STR$(M):
RETURN
3070 K=VAL(A$):IF K>J OR K<1 GOTO 3065
3075 CON$(N,I)=POSS$(M,K):RETURN
3080 PRINT "INPUT A NUMERIC CONSTANT BETWEEN    ";POSS$(M,1);" AND    ";POSS$
(M,2);" OR (O)BJECT"
3090 INPUT A$:IF A$="O" OR A$= "o" THEN GOSUB 3200:CON$(N,I)="*"+STR$(M):
RETURN
3095 CON$(N,I)=A$:RETURN
3100 REM INPUT ALL PROPOSITIONS IN RULE N
3110 I=1
3120 PRINT "PROPOSITION ";I: GOSUB 3000
3130 IF I=4 THEN RETURN
3140 INPUT"IS THERE ANOTHER PROPOSITION (Y/N)?    ";A$:IF A$="Y" THEN I=I+1:
GOTO 3120
3150 RETURN
3200 REM SELECT AN OBJECT
3210 PRINT "WHAT IS THE NUMBER OF THE OBJECT?    ":INPUT M
3220 IF M>NOBJS THEN PRINT "THIS OBJECT DOES NOT EXIST":GOTO 3210
3230 PRINT "OBJECT SELECTED IS ";NAM$(M)
3240 INPUT "IS THIS CORRECT? (Y/N)";A$
3250 IF A$="N" AND A$="n" GOTO 3210
3260 RETURN
4000 REM CONTROL OF EXECUTION
4010 GOSUB 4100
4020 RTOB=1:UPMOD=0:J=0:N=ACT(NCON):GOTO 4500
4040 NCON=NCON+1
4050 IF NCON<=NACTS GOTO 4020
4060 PRINT #1, "NO CONCLUSION CAN BE OFFERED TO THIS PROBLEM":GOSUB 200:
GOTO 100
4100 REM INITIALIZE
4110 NCON=1:NTOB=0:NTRL=0:NJ=0:CLS
4120 FOR I=1 TO Z:QSTAT$(I)="UNK":RES$(I)="UNK":RSTAT$(I)="UNK":NRL(I)=0
4130 FOR J=1 TO 4:PSTAT$(I,J)="UNK":NEXT J
4140 FOR J=1 TO 5:RULE(I,J)=0:NEXT J
4150 NEXT I
4200 FOR J=1 TO NRULS:N=CNUM(J):M=NRL(N)
4205 IF M<=8 GOTO 4220
4210 PRINT "ERROR!! MORE THAN 8 RULES REFER TO OBJECT ";N,NAM$(N)
4215 GOSUB 200: GOTO 100
4220 M=M+1:NRL(N)=M:RULE(N,M)=J
4230 NEXT J
4240 RETURN
4500 REM EVAL OBJECT N
4505 IF PR=1 AND UPMOD=0 THEN PRINT #1, "EVALUATING OBJECT    ";N,"    ",NAM$
(N)
4510 IF QSTAT$(N)="ANS" OR UPMOD=1 GOTO 4650
4520 IF TYP$(N)="Q" THEN GOSUB 5000:GOTO 4640
4525 IF TYP$(N)="N" THEN GOSUB 5100:GOTO 4640
4530 NJ=1
4535 J=RULE(N,NJ)
4540 IF RSTAT$(J)="F" GOTO 4590
4550 IF RSTAT$(J)="T" GOTO 4600
4560 RTRL=1:UPMOD=0
4570 GOTO 6000
4580 IF RSTAT$(J)="T" GOTO 4600
4590 NJ=NJ+1:IF NJ<=NRL(N) GOTO 4535
4595 IF PR=1 AND UPMOD=0 THEN PRINT #1, "NO RULES FOUND TO EVALUATE OBJECT
",NAM$(N)
```

```
4597 GOTO 4698
4600 RES$(N)=CRES$(J):QSTAT$(N)="ANS":IF TYP$(N)="SG" GOTO 4640
4610 PRINT #1, :PRINT #1, "THE CONCLUSION IS"
4620 PRINT #1, NAM$(N)," IS  ",RES$(N)
4630 INPUT "(H)OW OR PRESS RETURN TO CONTINUE ";A$: IF A$="H" OR A$="h"
     THEN GOSUB 5600
4635 GOTO 100
4640 GOTO 7000
4650 IF PR=1 AND UPMOD=0 THEN PRINT #1, "VALUE OF OBJECT    ";NAM$(N);"  IS
     ";RES$(N)
4698 ON RTOB GOTO 4040,6065,6110
5000 REM ASK A QUESTION
5020 PRINT :PRINT QTXT$(N):PRINT:K=1
5030 PRINT K,"  ",POSS$(N,K)
5040 IF POSS$(N,K+1)<>"" THEN K=K+1:GOTO 5030
5045 PRINT:PRINT SPC(10),"SELECT AN OPTION OR (W)HY"
5050 INPUT A$:IF A$="W" OR A$="w" THEN GOSUB 5500:GOTO 5000
5080 M=VAL(A$):IF M>K OR M<1 THEN PRINT "OUTSIDE RANGE":GOTO 5050
5090 RES$(N)=POSS$(N,M):QSTAT$(N)="ANS":RETURN
5100 REM ASK A NUMERICAL Q
5110 MU=VAL(POSS$(N,1)):ML=VAL(POSS$(N,2))
5115 PRINT :PRINT QTXT$(N):PRINT
5120 PRINT SPC(10),"INPUT A NUMBER BETWEEN  ";MU;" AND   ";ML;" OR (W)HY"
5130 INPUT A$:IF A$="W" OR A$="w" THEN GOSUB 5500:GOTO 5100
5140 M=VAL(A$):IF M>MU OR M<ML THEN PRINT "OUTSIDE RANGE":GOTO 5130
5150 RES$(N)=STR$(M):QSTAT$(N)="ANS":RETURN
5500 REM WHY IS OBJECT N BEING EVALUATED (BY RULE J)
5510 NW=N:JD=J:NTW=NTRL
5520 IF JD=0 THEN PRINT #1, "OBJECT ";NAM$(NW);" IS BEING EVALUATED BY THIS
     QUESTION":GOSUB 200:RETURN
5530 PRINT #1, "OBJECT ";NAM$(NW);" IS NEEDED TO EVALUATE THIS RULE (NO.";
     JD;")"
5540 OBN=0:GOSUB 8000:NW1=CNUM(JD)
5550 PRINT #1, "TO GIVE A VALUE TO ";NAM$(NW)
5560 INPUT "(W)HY OR PRESS RETURN ";A$
5570 IF A$="W" AND NTW<>0 THEN NW=NW1:JD=STKJ(NTW):NTW=NTW-1:GOTO 5520
5580 RETURN
5600 REM HOW WAS OBJECT N EVALUATED
5605 PRINT #1,
5610 IF QSTAT$(N)="UNK" THEN PRINT #1, "OBJECT ";NAM$(N);" HAS NO VALUE":
GOTO 5680
5620 IF TYP$(N)="G" OR TYP$(N)="SG" GOTO 5630
5625 PRINT #1, "OBJECT ";NAM$(N);" OF VALUE ";RES$(N);" WAS FOUND BY ASKING
     A QUESTION":GOTO 5680
5630 I=1
5640 JD=RULE(N,I): IF JD=0 THEN GOTO 5680
5650 IF RSTAT$(JD)<>"T" THEN I=I+1:GOTO 5640
5660 PRINT #1, "THE RULE USED TO EVALUATE ";NAM$(N);" WITH VALUE ";RES$(N);
" WAS"
5670 OBN=1:GOSUB 8000
5680 PRINT "INPUT ANY OBJECT NUMBER OR PRESS RETURN TO CONTINUE"
5690 INPUT A$: IF A$="" THEN RETURN
5695 N=VAL(A$):IF N<1 OR N>NOBJS GOTO 5690
5699 GOTO 5605
6000 REM EVALUATE RULE J (UNKNOWN)
6005 IF PR=1 AND UPMOD=0 THEN PRINT #1, "EVALUATING RULE    ";J
6010 NTOB=NTOB+1:STKN(NTOB)=N:RETOBJ(NTOB)=RTOB:I=1
6020 IF RSTAT$(J)<>"UNK" GOTO 6250
6022 IF PSTAT$(J,I)="F" THEN RSTAT$(J)="F":GOTO 6250
6025 I=I+1:IF NUM(J,I)<>0 GOTO 6022
6027 I=1
6030 IF PSTAT$(J,I)="T" GOTO 6180
6050 RTOB=2:GOSUB 6300
6060 N=NUM(J,I):GOTO 4500
6065 GOSUB 6320
6067 IF QSTAT$(N)="UNK" GOTO 6250
6070 A$=RES$(N):B$=CONS(J,I)
6080 IF ASC(B$)<>42 GOTO 6120
6090 N=VAL(MID$(B$,2,2))
6100 RTOB=3:GOSUB 6300:GOTO 4500
6110 GOSUB 6320:B$=RES$(N):IF QSTAT$(N)="UNK" GOTO 6250
```

```
6120 M=OP(J,I):GOSUB 6370
6160 PSTAT$(J,I)=P$
6170 IF P$="F" THEN RSTAT$(J)="F":GOTO 6250
6180 I=I+1:IF NUM(J,I)<>0 GOTO 6030
6200 RSTAT$(J)="T":A$=RTYP$(J)
6210 IF A$="G" OR A$="SG" GOTO 6250
6220 IF A$="*ASK" THEN M=N:N=CNUM(J):GOSUB 6500:N=M:GOTO 6250
6230 IF A$="*DISPLAY" THEN PRINT :PRINT CRES$(J):GOTO 6250
6250 IF PR=1 AND UPMOD=0 THEN PRINT #1, "STATUS OF RULE    ";J;"  IS    ";
RSTAT$(J)
6298 N=STKN(NTOB):RTOB=RETOBJ(NTOB):NTOB=NTOB-1
6299 ON RTRL GOTO 4580,7040
6300 REM ON RULE STACK
6310 NTRL=NTRL+1:STKNJ(NTRL)=NJ:STKI(NTRL)=I:STKJ(NTRL)=J:STKA$(NTRL)=A$:RE
TRUL(NTRL)=RTRL:RETURN
6320 REM OFF RULE STACK
6330 NJ=STKNJ(NTRL):I=STKI(NTRL):J=STKJ(NTRL):A$=STKA$(NTRL):RTRL=RETRUL(NT
RL):NTRL=NTRL-1:RETURN
6370 REM EVAL PROP
6375 AX=VAL(A$):BX=VAL(B$):P$="F"
6380 ON M GOTO 6400,6410,6420,6430,6440,6450,6440,6450,6460,6470
6400 IF AX=BX THEN P$="T":RETURN
6405 RETURN
6410 IF AX<BX THEN P$="T":RETURN
6415 RETURN
6420 IF AX>BX THEN P$="T":RETURN
6425 RETURN
6430 IF AX<>BX THEN P$="T":RETURN
6435 RETURN
6440 IF A$=B$ THEN P$="T":RETURN
6445 RETURN
6450 IF A$<>B$ THEN P$="T":RETURN
6455 RETURN
6460 IF AX<=BX THEN P$="T":RETURN
6465 RETURN
6470 IF AX>=BX THEN P$="T":RETURN
6475 RETURN
6500 IF TYP$(N)="Q" THEN GOSUB 5000:RETURN
6510 IF TYP$(N)="N" THEN GOSUB 5100:RETURN
7000 REM DO UPDATE
7005 IF PR=1 THEN PRINT #1, "UPDATING"
7010 UPMOD=1:RTRL=2:J=1
7020 IF RSTAT$(J)<>"UNK" GOTO 7075
7030 GOTO 6000
7040 IF RSTAT$(J)<>"T" GOTO 7075
7045 IF PR=1 THEN PRINT #1,"RULE ";J;" IS NOW TRUE"
7050 N=CNUM(J):IF RTYP$(J)="G" GOTO 4600
7055 IF RTYP$(J)="SG" THEN RES$(N)=CRES$(J):QSTAT$(N)="ANS":GOTO 7000
7060 IF RTYP$(J)="*ASK" GOTO 7000
7075 IF PR=1 THEN PRINT #1, "RULE ",J,"  ",RSTAT$(J)
7080 J=J+1:IF J<=NRULS GOTO 7020
7085 UPMOD=0:GOTO 4650
8000 REM DISPLAY RULE JD WITH/WITHOUT OBJECT NO.S
8010 A$="IF   ":I=1
8020 C$=CON$(JD,I):BN$="("+STR$(NUM(JD,I))+")"
8025 IF ASC(C$)=42 THEN M=VAL(MID$(C$,2)):C$=NAM$(M):CN$="("+STR$(M)+")"
8030 IF OBN=0 THEN BN$="":CN$=""
8040 PRINT #1, A$,NAM$(NUM(JD,I));BN$;"  ";OPR$(OP(JD,I));"  ";C$;CN$
8050 A$="AND ":B$="  ":I=I+1
8060 IF NUM(JD,I)<>0 GOTO 8020
8070 BN$="":IF OBN<>0 THEN BN$="("+STR$(CNUM(JD))+")"
8080 PRINT #1, "  ",NAM$(CNUM(JD));BN$;" IS ";CRES$(JD):PRINT #1,
8090 RETURN
```

Appendix 3 — Some shell programs

SAVOIR — developed by I.S.I. Ltd, England.
This shell is a clear descendant from the early system PROSPECTOR offering rules, demons and a representation of uncertainty as discussed in Chapter 9. The shell is written in PASCAL and runs on PC's and certain main frames.

ENVISAGE (or SD-ADVISER) — developed by Systems Designers plc., England.
This shell also has its roots in PROSPECTOR and has a particularly clear version of the Bayes statement. It has structuring to its rules and powerful control over the inferencing by a procedural language. It is available on PC's and certain mainframes.

LEONARDO — developed by Creative Logic Ltd, England.
This is a good example of a shell with a simple, readable form of rule with facilities for structuring the rule set and for structuring objects by frames. It is written in FORTRAN and runs on PC's and certain mainframes.

GOLDWORKS — developed by Gold Hill Computers Inc., U.S.A.
A large and complex system based on very powerful and flexible definitions of frame objects, but with a less than readable form of rule. Written in LISP, it runs on PC's with 8 MB memory or on AI work stations. It is a good example of an expert system development environment.

Index